The Literary Parrot:
series one

Editors
Dustin Pickering
Mutiu Olawuyi

TRANSCENDENT ZERO PRESS
HOUSTON, TEXAS

ISBN-13: 978-1-946460-33-2

Published in the United States of America

Transcendent Zero Press
16429 El Camino Real Apt. #7
Houston, TX 77062

The Literary Parrot:
series one

Editors
Dustin Pickering
Mutiu Olawuyi

Acknowledgements

The initiators of this quarterly literary project are indebted to all the authors who shared their works. We would like to especially thank Leah Maines at Finishing Line Press, and Prolific Pulse Press for providing us with a wealth of poets and writers to interview.

A list of our donors deserve mention:

Maria Nazos, Emily Fortney Blunt, Linda Trott Dickman, W. Ruth Kozak, Dennis Brown, Madeline Artenberg, Jerena Tobiasen, Rick Christiansen, Casey Dorman, Olga Zolle, Paul Stroble, Angie Mack, and Kelle Grace Gaddis. Without you, the New York Literary Corner would be much smaller.

Introduction from the editors

The Literary Parrot is a quarterly anthology initiated by the Chief Editor and Producer/Director of New York Parrot/Parrot TV, Mutiu Olawuyi, and the host of Parrot Literary Corner, Dustin Pickering. The anthology publishes unique works of featured guests on the only TV show on earth for creative writers and a few selected published creative writers on New York Parrot website.

This anthology is an explosive mix of positive, invigorating poetry by contemporary poets and imaginative prose writers from around the globe. We have also included several images as well: photographs by Brian Kehinde, Bill Arnott, Melissa Chappell, Emily Blunt Fortney, and Sandra Feen; paintings or drawings by Wolf Man, Bengt O. Björklund and many others in the realm of visual art. Among the poets included are veterans and heavy hitters of the scene such as Wang Ping, Ron Whitehead, Marc Olmsted, and John Dorsey, as well as a great mix of prose contemporaries such as Panagiota Bleta and Raymond Walker. There are some fresher voices such as Sushant Thapa, Howard Stein, and Suchismita Ghoshal. The list of writers we've included is massive in this book accumulating over 200 pages.

Bear in mind that most of the poets and writers included in this anthology have appeared on our TV broadcast New York Parrot Literary Corner, as seen on YouTube. You can access their interviews via https://m.youtube.com/channel/UCqeMsHoqgwNc5Oaz1TPim3g. Our guests are unique in multiple respects: they are outspoken, adventurous, hard-working minds and bodies promoting the spirit of literature and ideas, and they are globally oriented. Some of them are university professors, poet laureates, established literary award winners, popular artists, et ceterar. Countries represented include Nigeria, Nepal, Croatia, Slovakia, Jamaica, Scotland. Poland, Romania, South Korea, Israel, India, Bangladesh, Tanzania, United States of America, Canada, France, Italy, Greece, Germany, Sweden, China, and Uzbekistan. We apologize if we have missed anyone. This anthology reaches across national and even continental boundaries to support the global audience.

Others included in the second section were published at newyorkparrot.com at our Literacy Corner. The works were selected for their relevance to current events or socially oriented themes. New York Parrot seeks work that addresses issues such as climate change, natural disasters, Covid, social justice, racial and economic justice, prison reforms, comments on news stories in literary form, creative commentaries of satire or criticism, and other culturally difficult subject matter. These topics are not easy to consider in the sublime form of poetry. New York Parrot understands and appreciates all our writers for their effort.

A fair amount of tedium was involved on my part as editor of this project. We thank all our guests and those who brave the void to submit to the website. Your effort and time are invaluable to us. We may include you in future volumes.

Many of these authors are also involved in social activism. Their work is greatly appreciated.

Finally, we hope you spend time with these works. This is a treasured volume.

Dustin Pickering
Mutiu Olawuyi

CONTENTS

PUBLISHED ON WEBSITE

PICTORALS

Welcome guests from *NEW YORK PARROT*
Literary Corner...

Photo of Andre Just Sais at The Shed Open Mic

by Brian Kehinde

Denja Abdullahi
GOREE'S WAVES

Waves,
What untold stories
Lie beneath your surface?
Can you tell the names
Of those rebellious ones
Who saw no life beyond here?
Can you map the silent tears or loud wails
Of those who braced for the unknown?

Goree, what are you today?
Conclave of old bricks
With a history full of scents?
Canvass for crazy artists
In search of formless forms?

Goree, how much of you is real?
How much is fried and salted
For the corrupted tastes of tourists
Hankering after a lachrymose history?

Waves of questions,
For the beach bums
For the café rats
For the taverns
For the African Picassos
To fill a dug-out canoe
And set sail with.

* Goree is an Island on the Coast of Senegal in Africa where African slaves were briefly
quartered before been shipped to the new world during the Trans Atlantic Slave Trade
Era.

A'zam Abidov
I WILL MISS YOU

I am so sorry to see that neither your existence as a human being nor your dead body is worthy of something in this country. What an earth you have come to this world, poor man! Anyway, did you not deserve tactful attitude towards yourself, at least now? My heart shrunk when they turned me upside down and kicked me to the mess. Moreover, one gets sick of the smell of the rags I have been wrapped up. Or have I started to smell bad in two days? Oh boy, the bus trunk became a shelter for me to take me home when I died!

My friend barely persuaded a bus driver, since none of them agreed to take the dead body. It looked like this driver was with good heart, or he just assented out of desperation, seeing swollen teary eyes of my friend. "OK, but you pay for the usual passenger, not the luggage!" the driver said. Otherwise, in addition to my humiliation, my body would rot in these lands…

I remember my past life. What a happy youth I had! Or the first years of our wedding and times when I scented my wife's handkerchief while waiting for her to come from cotton fields very late in the evenings. Or hot summer days when my wife's little nephew and I swam in the small river of a remote village, where we resided temporarily to take care of my old parents-in-law…

The bus is flying fast. From time to time the trunk door opens and I see the lanterns of border guards. My face was exposed in the movement. As we go, suddenly I feel the banana box next to me shake. There's another big bundle on top of the box, you can't tell what's inside, but it looks like something very heavy. As the banana box is moved with effort, the bundle slides down. I notice someone lifting his head from the box.

One can hardly accommodate himself in this trunk, sitting or lying, or you can take a dead man like me, but I can see in the flashlight that the thing that has just raised its head is a 12- or 13-year-old boy! When the trunk opens for checkup, he lies down wrapped in a fabric with an effort not to be seen. I think, when the light came on, the little boy saw me… It seems that he came to work to this country, but failed, so without a penny, he agreed to be a "luggage" to go home in this trunk. I can feel him shivering from the cold. Or is that out of fear? But he felt a little relieved that someone was around. However, as he slides towards me, he tries to rub my face; he strokes and pulls my mustache, my stiff mustache! My frozen body! Sensing my death, he screams, *Voy Dod!* Luckily no one hears it in a good noise, but who knows if there is any screaming in the ears of some sleepy, drunken, cold men and women sitting in the passenger compartment of the bus. The boy, going side by side with a corpse like me, may be thankful for his survival, but it is impossible not to endure it. We have been driving for 3 days together. It was as if the boy had stuffed a loaf of bread in his pocket, and from time to time I heard a squeaking noise.

Again past times come to my mind. Oh, I remember my daughters! My princesses! They work in the evening shifts in black sweat for a pittance to help the family! Your dad went to work to bring a bag of money, but how are you going to meet me now, my dears?! Wouldn't I see these days if I had a son? Ah, strangers will take me to my tomb now…

The bus stopped. A familiar Uzbek voice is heard from the radio: *"News from Heaven! Thousands of jobs have been created! Millions of young and old people are satisfied with the just policy pursued by the leader of our country!"* The messages are accompanied by songs and melodies: *Yallama yorim yallo-la, yallola-shaylik, yallola-shaylik! Let's split into three or four and chat and grieve!!!*

17

My sobbing relatives take me through the pass to a remote village three hundred kilometers away.

My wife Samira, my orphan Samira! I indeed missed you so much! I wish I could wipe your bitter tears off. I want to caress your face, I want to kiss your callous hands – do you feel it too? My lips can't move, only my mouth is stiff, and my body has already started stinking.

Fortunately, it snowed today, and the weather is much colder. But there was still no gas, and the corpse-washer was washing me with the water boiled on the fireplace. Well, such water is very sweet, isn't it? Just let me take a bath in fresh sweet water and wrap my whole body in white cloth…

The snow is playing and falling on my shroud. It is crying and falling on the velvet cover and I'm not cold anymore. And my lips don't blush anymore. I just miss you, Samira! We will see each other in doomsday now, my Samira! Be safe until the Day of Judgment! I miss you!

Sarfraz Ahmed
AND THEN THEY DANCED

Like silhouettes,
Flickering through the trees,
Like the early morning breeze,
Like waves crashing on the shore,
Like a crowd wanting more,
Like a field of tulips in spring,
They danced gave it everything,

Crucifying and dying,
With every limb intact,
They danced like acrobats in midflow,
Like eagles flying,
With nowhere to go,

They held on for dear life,
As limbs began to contract and subcontract,
Elasticated, every movement,
Clenched their muscles in release,
Dancing for freedom,
Dancing for love,
Dancing for beauty,
In a world that longed for more,
They wrapped their wings around each other,
And into the heavens they began to soar.

Bil Arnott
FROM A SHORELINE SLIVER, WARMED BY MORNING SUN

A gap between two driftwood branches, bleached, sea-scoured
turned to silver white. A rising sun reflects, the sea a sparkle
amber shades the tree once bled. Its nectar, honey-coloured
seeping slow, a treacle trail of tears, of joy, as though the world
just now has learned all that we know. The scrunch of pebble
underfoot, a fringe of sea foam in the same wan yellow hues
of ocean sun, in ancient amber wounds and earthen golden glitter
flickering in streambeds feeding to the sea. Where salmon, in their
silver speckled sheen like birch trees, pass beyond the rapids, beaver
dams, impediments and humans, from the saline through the eddies
brown and brackish to the fresh stream rivulets and creeks to spawn
and then pass on, same as the timber slowly perishing in seaside sun.

Madeline Artenberg
SUPPER TIME

Our mother never cooked
like our grandmother did,
her mother, Katie,
with ingredients from scratch
took an hour to prepare,
a whole morning to get done,
filling the apartment
with warmth.

Our mother reduced food
to its driest, flattest state; broiled
what should have been babied
on top of the stove,
or tenderly minded inside.

Our mother would throw under the broiler
flesh or fish, never look until edges curled
into the same brown, no matter what
it started out as, until
it toughened up like a wrestler
punching our teeth and gums
as we tried to chew.
No sauce on top,
no salt, no spices.

We couldn't talk much for all the effort needed
to eat the halibut or dry white chicken.
We couldn't complain,
couldn't ask for things we weren't getting,
like allowance or summer camp,
couldn't plead with her to stop hitting us,
stop screaming;
all we could do was chew and chew,
get through supper time.

Don Beukes
FORBIDDEN PASSION

The allure of you makes me feel a
red-hot smouldering hue – It
burns slowly churns at my very core
as I try my best to contain it but my body is
weak. I cannot deny this fiery streak
consuming me so surprisingly welcoming
yet you are totally unaware of my
desiring laser stare as you touch me
lightly to signal my momentary patience
whilst you say your goodbyes unaware of
my inner cries to hold you grab you
embrace you and to never let go in this
timeless sensuous slow motion fresco...

Bengt O. Björklund

suddenly in awe I and the day
hesitate to add molestation
to the wild mix of wind and shadows
returning all bones to the table

there are goals billowing
windows calling your name
summer is a slow hand
hesitating above taut skin

seeded by voracity and flames
mothers breastfeed the sun
lingering in my chains I turn
all tomorrows into the hum of ash

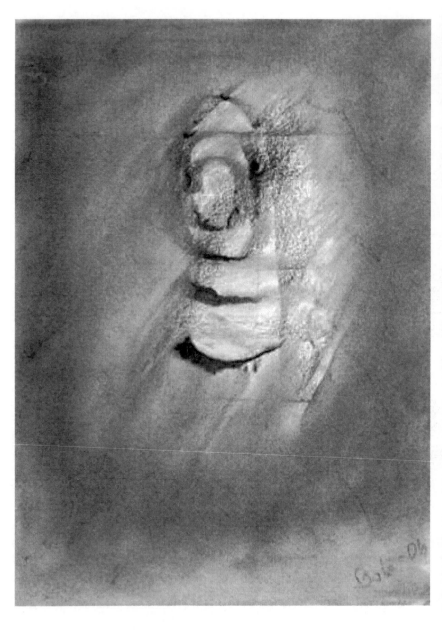

Artwork pages 24-25 by Bengt O. Björklund

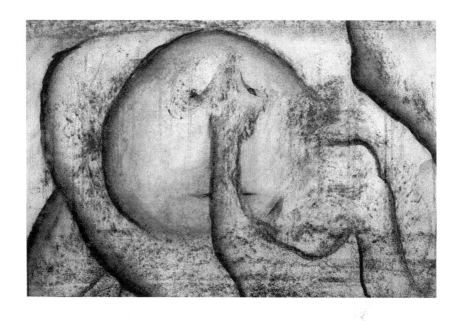

Panagiota Bleta
PROFIT IS NOT AN ACHIEVEMENT

It's not a praise the bloody economy I have created. It is not an achievement the profit that I do not feel in my body, which is empty of emotion. It is not an achievement the siege of my memory. It is not an achievement the adulteration of reality. It is not an achievement the nature that is not nature. It is not an achievement the truth that is not true. Democracy, which is not a democracy, is not an achievement. It is not an achievement what detracts my desire. And I cannot cry, nor laugh. A big gap I have in my mind and stomach...

Emily Fortney Blunt
BUILDING BRIDGES

I heard radio hosts talking the other day

about hope

About how it lies in God's hands,

lives in the Land of Wishful Thinking,
is offered up,
full of wanting
that for which it's holding out

A word asking for

something,
someone
to get us through- into- beyond
where we are now

The way we've carried hope

sometimes implies
there's nothing to be done

except wait for an outcome

But the Bridge Builders know-

Hope is an action word

They see the struggle

in crossing rough waters
knowing a few will make it easily
across the rapids,
some will drown
while the currents pull all others

away from the whole

And so…

The Engineers of Crossing-Difficult-Terrain

begin their work-
creating the hoped for passage

over the River of Despair

Can you do this? Ask...

"What work can my hope do?"

You don't have to build the bridge-

that work has already been done

Maybe though

you could walk your hope across it
one tentative step at a time

Building Bridges: Bluewater Bridge
Emily Fortney Blunt

Dennis Brown
TO LIGHT MY WAY

Do not look into my eyes
For these tears I cannot hide
I am blinded by your mere decision
As your love for me has slowly died

Banish me from your barren heart
And erase the memories of yesteryear
For I'll no longer live among your thoughts
As you live your life without me near

Release me from your final grip
Watch me fall and let me be
So I can find what you tossed away
And place it back inside of me

I'll learn to heal myself again
And regain the strength I used to know
As I head down a path of gradual hope
That will lead me to where I need to go

When I finally reach my destination
I'll stop and look up towards the night
To find that star that I wished upon
That lit my way and gave me sight

James Bryant's
DARK HAIKU

Blinded by the pain
I can't see, for the Dead Sea
pouring from my eyes

A crushing defeat
my heart, like bittersweet grapes
dying on the vine

Photo of Odin Wotan taken from *greekmythology.com*

Dr. Troy Camplin
STENO'S LAMENT

My sister raped by cruel Poseidon, sea
That swirled between her thighs--and I stood by
My sister--so I shared her fate. Men flee
Before my stare, for if they catch my eye
To milky marble they'll become--I stand
Them in my garden, stony sentinel
To warn away the wise and wary. Hand
Of bronze will bring my sculpture garden full
Of mutilated men. And yet, she's gone--
My sister, murdered by a mortal man--
Her scaly torso prone, the light of dawn
Reflecting in the blood that, headless, ran.
My gorgeous, gory garden can't assuage
My guilt, eternal guilt, eternal age.

Dr. Troy Camplin
THE ODIN WITHIN

Thought and memory are flying through the sky--
Black-clad ravens which will never die--
Over all of man this pair will fly,
Bringing knowledge to deep wisdom's only due.

Skaldic mead has quenched my thirst for many years,
Bought by suffering, pain, bane, and tears--
Yet, this honeyed drink has sent my fears
Down to Hell--I brought back up the songs man hears.

Darlene Campos
ABUELITA IS EIGHTY-ONE*

Abuelita is eighty-one
but in her world, she's thirty-five or

sometimes younger

and she can't remember if she already
made her kids breakfast or if she's late
to open her convenience store.

Abuelita is eighty-one
and in her mind, Abuelito is still alive,
he must be working late at his dental office
on a patient with an infected tooth.

When her brain lets her, she can speak
so she calls out his name, but he never
comes around and for a moment

she remembers the harsh truth.

Abuelita is eighty-one
but in her world, she's young and
healthy and raising a family.
For now, she can live in a different era

just like the rest of us desire to.

*Photo accompanying on page 35

Previously published in Heartland Society of Women Writers

Abuelita at her first communion. Guayaquil, Ecuador, December 1947.

Photo by Melissa Chappell

Rick Christiansen
ERODED HIP HOP COMPLEX

I.
KRUNK!
Say the dust motes falling into the sunlight before me.
An act of becoming and dissolving.
Our death is our wedding with these things.
I feel it in the firmness of each footstep taken.
And myself, in the lifting of that step.
The artisan searches for what is not there
In order to practice his craft.
I practice stillness in my movement.
I am not there.

II.
KRUNK!
Say the joints that ache while they dance through the floor.
Anxiety makes ME warm.
And so, I contribute to the process.
I make trinkets to prove that I exist.
I display them to force their existence.
Even tea will intoxicate.
If only you drink it quickly.
The body will nurture the mind and provide
bad advisement.

III.
KRUNK!
Say the utensils that I have laid down after their use
I am much too small a place to live.
I must stretch and groan into fullness.
I have pulled my own existence out of this fissure.
I have not forgotten the traces of my gifts.
I remember the poverty of emptiness.
I will not travel there again.
The flavor of optimism builds on my tongue.
And I swallow.

Previously published in Oddball Magazine 3-8-16

Lyn Coffin
LIPOGRAM*: THE TREE BY THE WINDOW

I determine its destiny in the world,
but the tree is not mindful of my power.
Its boughs torment me, whispering
insidious rumors: I whistle to let it
know I love it only to
the limited extent to which
one lets oneself love outside things.
When it's evening, this twisted tree
bows to the shrinking light: it seems
to be subservient but under
cover of submission, the tree's
fingers begin their tremulous
liberties, touching my window
lasciviously. The tree seems determined
to insert itself where it doesn't belong:
it smiles when it strokes the cold solidity
keeping it out. Then, when the outside
light is gone, evening slides
through my window into my room
riding the boughs of this duplicitous
tree that wind me in tendrils like
some serpent, choking me with sticky green love.

a poem that leaves out one letter

Pat Connors
BECOMING

> *it is always becoming a poem*
> *this furnace, this fire*
> *in a corner of the body's dark*
>
> *this is the place that burns*
> *whatever has been broken*

"Heart", by Mick Burrs

The world says
we are the result
of the residue
it leaves upon us.

Don't let this be.
Burn this dross from me!
No matter the pain it brings
I will not be like everyone else.

Mould me in your image
form me in the refiner's crucible
that my thoughts, my work
and my poetry may bring you glory.

Let all the indescribable pain
endured while becoming understandable
bring clarity to my vision
and integrity to my life.

Then my words would blaze
a trail across the midnight sky
and be a likeness of the light
which will forever shut out darkness.

Notes on Prior Publication of "Becoming" by Pat Connors

"Becoming" was previously published in *Tending the Fire*, a chapbook of the League of Canadian Poets, in May 2020; Lummox 9 Anthology, released by Lummox Press in November 2020; and *The Celebration of Poetry 20th Anniversary Anthology*, published by Beret Days Press in March 2021.

I wrote this in honour of Mick Burrs, who was my editor for several years last decade.

He passed away on April 20, 2021, ten days after his 81st birthday.

David Cope
A DESPERATE MOTHER

almost in tears after hours in stores with empty
shelves, empty coolers—no milk for her babes,

no toilet paper nor wipes after fearful hoarders had
grabbed everything and run for the registers.

The old man could not help, suggested she return
in the morning when the store restocks shelves—

"come early" while these others sleep. In the morning
he returned for his own distilled water and milk,

the shelves restocked, he wondering how she'd
gotten through the night, if she'd found her way.

Photo by Brian Kehinde

Joshua Corwin
12:01 AM

I can hear the shine in your eyes
on the other end of the telephone.

When I speak like this,
I feel authentic
and not heavy.

I don't have to tattoo meaning in the air
to know what you mean.

I remember when you first told me…
apropos of nothing…
about the different levels of charitable donation.

I was sitting right across from you — over there.
(You in that armchair, me in this one: our eyes.)

You said there's the donor who gives large sums
and puts a placard on the wall, signifying
who it's from;

and then there's the other one who gives…
but remains anonymous.

Your words hanging like a phantom,
I didn't have to be who I thought I was;

you were once me,
once where I was…

In that moment, I knew.

PUBLISHED IN *BECOMING VULNERABLE*
First appeared in *Al-Khemia Poetica*. September 3, 2019.
Nominated for 2020 Pushcart Prize.
Reprinted in *The Ephimilar Journal*, *Palisadian-Post* (print),
Autism Special Interest Group of British MENSA (print),
poeticdiversity (online) and *Sequoyah Cherokee River Journal* (online).
Translated in Sequoyah Cherokee syllabus, Georgian and Hebrew.

David Haotian Dai

LOVE PREVAILS OVER HATE

Freezing wind of hate
Gusts out from cold blood.
And hatred breeds from frozen hearts.
People like angry animals
Fight against each other

A voice from Heaven echoes
My lost sheep,
Come back to me
You will have love and peace

Oh! the love from God
Like sunshine in the winter
Lights up the darkness of peoples' hearts
And dissolves the ice of selfishness.
People return to he Kingdom of God
Filled with peace and joy
And Love each other
Just like brothers and sisters

Oh! the power of love
So intense as burning fire
Melts the iceberg of hate.
And light up the kindness in our hearts

Linda Trott Dickman
QUEEN ANNE'S LACE

The bloom of Anne, who wove
the most slender of threads
into delicate laces.
Her finger pricked, a single drop

of blood fell, crimson on center.
Such elegance in the breeze
Happy to grow where ever it may
this faux carrot, fit for a Queen,

A queen of the cinema.
Springs up independently,
Like Hepburn, who berated
any gardener for weeding

it out. Quintessential Kate.
Young roots best for cooking,
popular wildflower of brides.
Echoing the sleeves, *decolletage*.

Just as elegant in the wake
of the ceremony, between my teeth,
on the floor
of the bridal suite.

Casey Dorman
DEATH AND THE OLD MAN

"You get to make a decision." The doctor's freshly scrubbed face smiled down at him, the young man's eyes glittering with delight. Sydney knew the doctor was trying to be supportive, because that was the mission of Happy Acres hospice care facility. Sydney found it intrusive. The last thing he needed was a bunch of strangers trying to ease his *passing*, as they called it. He hated the term. He wasn't passing from one place to another; he wasn't going anywhere. He just wouldn't *be* anymore.

"Sherbet or ice-cream?" Sydney asked, raising a skeptical eyebrow. Frankly, he was tired of meaningless decisions. Chicken or beef (both ground into flavorless mash that reminded him of his dreaded childhood porridge)? Shower or bath (neither preferable to staying in bed)? Happy Acres tried to give everyone maximum control of their lives, not wanting them to *pass* while feeling powerless. Sydney *was* powerless; he couldn't halt the inexorable arrival of death.

"I'm talking about a real choice, Sydney." Dr. Moncrieff's smile was gone, his eyes serious. He leaned forward, explaining that, three hours before Sydney was to die, they could give him one of three mind-altering drugs, strong enough to last until the moment of his death. One would stimulate his thinking, sharpening his reasoning while enlivening his imagination. Enough time to finish his novel, Sydney thought, the one he had been working on for the last six years and which was almost complete. The second drug soothed his nervous system while intensifying his senses. He thought about listening to his treasured recordings of classical music, slipping away in the midst of a Beethoven pastoral. The third drug directly activated his brain's pleasure center. The thought of being consumed by intense pleasure, right up to the moment of his death, caused a stir in Sydney he hadn't felt in years. Dr. Moncrieff told him experimental subjects given this option said it was like a "three-hour orgasm."

He knew he should make the most of the time he had left, but what did that even mean? His wife was dead, so were his brother and sister. He had no children to say goodbye to. A random act of kindness? He couldn't even get out of bed by himself. He thought about his three options.

Sydney was an accomplished and lauded novelist. He was certain that if he could complete his latest novel, *Returning Home*, it would earn a Pulitzer Prize. His legacy as a writer would be firmly anchored, his name enshrined in American letters, his finest writing indelibly inscribed on paper, secured for posterity in the digital cloud. But what good were such outcomes if he were not there to enjoy them? He thought about the experience of writing, hearing the sentences in his head, seeing them flow onto the paper, experiencing that peak moment of the perfect wedding of sound and meaning that was the reason he wrote, the feeling of connection with something beyond himself. A feeling to die for.

But he also enjoyed music, enjoyed it immensely—Mahler's fourth symphony, with the second movement in which the violins, in the composer's words, "play us up to heaven." Schubert's *Death and the Maiden*, with its complex interplay of viola, violin and cello, its alternating *piano* and *fortissimo*, lyrical and stormy—it could make him feel as if he were transcending his physical being.

But if feeling pleasure was the answer—and what better way to spend his last hours than feeling intensely happy—why not experience it even more directly? A three-hour orgasm. He shivered at the thought. The evolutionary drive stripped down to its bare essence. Forget transcendence; everything but sexual pleasure was sublimation. Or was it? His sexual appetite had waned in the last years, but he'd not felt less pleasure. He enjoyed writing and listening to music even more than he had when he was younger. He closed his eyes. The choice was an impossible one. Then he laughed, felt his muscles relax, enjoyed the softness of the feather pillow beneath his head. Three beautiful options. Any of the three would please him. And even better, each choice was the right choice, because *it was his last choice.* And afterward? There was no *afterward*. No chance to feel regret, to wish he had chosen differently, to feel dissatisfied. The nothingness of death is complete. He opened his eyes and smiled up at Dr. Moncrieff.

"Have you got a coin?"

John Dorsey
AN EASTER POEM IN IRWIN, PENNSYLVANIA

they would line us up
in the parking lot
of the old hills department store

covered in fake green grass
& plastic eggs filled with penny candies
blowing a whistle
to start things off

we'd claw at each other
the closer we got

tufts of hair
& some light bruising
were a small price to pay

easter egg hunts
were how the romans
first developed a taste for blood
during the great
cabbage patch kid
craze of 1982

minutes later
sunlight poured down
on the ancient ruins
of a suburban strip mall

where we had lived
like yellow chicks squawking
in plastic baskets

the air still cool
the world went quiet
in the back
of a ford escort.

Robin Wyatt Dunn
LEENANE

I'm afraid; sometimes the sound is enough. The way the drums come in over the water. I was born here but I don't know the place—I don't have the knack for it. Sometimes I understand what we have done, in coming here, to the edge of the sea. It is a good and necessary thing, like death. Respectful, like. To be interred and stand there in the ground, awaiting paradise.

The sea is a black maw, mother. My only home. Tell me: is it true that I will die? I haven't yet. Sometimes I dream of it, the places beyond this world. The way they color the sky. That scares me too: how one world keeps bleeding over into another. They are not separate. What does it mean then to die?

It is no good to write, or, it is the best thing. Either way I know it is important, good or bad. I needed to tell you about this place.

It is a golden light in the afternoon but we hide from it inside, with our instruments. It is at night we go out, into the rain, or sometimes during the day when there is no sun, and the sky is a black cloud, covering the water. I like it best like that: mother is so close. The near and rich color of her skin.

Shaking against the rocks.

I am a kind of cripple: that is what the world has made me into. Still, that is not important here. Anyone can come here; you don't need any special skills. But it is not everyone who stays.

What can you see inside of light? It transmits a lot of information. Densely encoded. It is like a groups of thoughts, sent from somewhere else to cover the world we live inside of. And these places are then like dreams: rooms you can come into, in something else's mind.

I am afraid of that too. But that is all right; I like it too. To know I am important, and small, wedged against the black sea.

We have a theramin; its alien voice is important to me because it helps to describe how I came to know this place. You see I lied, or forgot—but that is all right. I do know the place—just a very small part of it. Although know is the wrong word too . . .

I am inside of it is the thing. It covers my entire body, the sound of the drums and trumpets.

Of course it has a "normal" history of kings and empires and ships coming and the peoples who made it how it is. None of that is true—or very little of it—but it gives it a veneer which is important. The little seaside village. Part of some greater thing. At night it is something else. Or even during the day, if you are willing to look.

Where we come alive in the dark to sing.

I sing to you too, though I am wrong and broken and miserable, a kind of flesh offering. Pauper for coins. Please sir, I have found a place for you to look at. Only twenty bob. It shines like a jewel. It covers my face like a veil. I am a dark water, streaming out from it.

Please sir, this is the place, my home. I am dead inside but it revives me, like oxygen into the brain. I stir and dance over the graves. Tell me, will you, if it gives you pleasure as it does to me? The empty sea and the trees washed in the blowing rain. Like a woman in distress, tearing at her hair.

I implore you; look out to the region near the edge, where we are huddled, singing.

Kelly Ann Ellis
A WOMAN ON THE FRINGE

Several years, ago, my (then) fifteen-year-old daughter Maddie told me that women who dislike pink and "feminine" attire are misogynists because they have internalized society's prejudices against women. The result is internalized self-loathing and subsequent rejection of the traditional accoutrements of being female.

Since Maddie is now my "offspring" and "she" is now "they," I wonder, is this true? And if so, is their wanting to surgically remove their breasts also misogynist in nature? They are more than willing to answer that question and even address the ones I haven't yet asked.

I am sometimes annoyed at being lectured on gender by a 22 year-old. I like to think I'm woke enough, what with grad school and podcasts and watching Roxanne Gay on Masterclass. But really, what the hell do I know? Despite bra-burnings and the well-meaning efforts of Betty Friedan and Gloria Steinem, I don't think most women of my generation were all that eager to reject the trappings of womanhood. Why would we? The only power I remember having as a young woman was tied to being beautiful. Of course, that power dissipated as my looks faded. Am I supposed to believe that the power I have now is tied to being invisible? Just how does that work, anyway?

A few years ago, I started wearing fringes because they were in style. They reminded me of the free-spirited sixties fashions of my childhood. I was six in 1966. Now I'm over sixty. I have a royal blue, glittery pancho that I love to wear, but my daughters tell me it reminds them of Lisa Frank. Lisa Frank, of the dolphins and rainbows that flourished in my household with three pre-teen girls growing up in the 90s. Back then, my daughters seemed to feel empowered by the dolphins, the rainbows, and the occasional shimmering unicorn, but now they urge me to eschew glitter, avoid fringe.

I have seen women draw a line in the glitter.

Recently I made the mistake of ordering skin care from an acquaintance who sells Mary Kay and since then, the cult has been after me in full force. I am lured to watch 7-minute videos with promises of free mascara. Who can resist that? But the testimonials are delivered by women wearing so much glitter that I start to think I'm trapped in Barbie's dream house, and I find myself looking down my beady bifocals at these women. "Empowered" is a word they like to use. But how can that be true? I don't have a problem with pink cars, but pink lipstick? My lips are disappearing as I speak.

I think I might be turning into a misogynist. Perhaps I have started to reject the tropes of femininity because I have internalized cultural messages that women are less-than, and this has translated into shame and self-loathing. Maybe. But I've also internalized a second set of messages that say beauty is power and the more beauty you put on, the more power you acquire. So I vacillate between putting on my face and facing down the put-on, the fake, the masquerade.

I am too old to think about this. Who is looking anyhow? I am at the age that women are deemed invisible. Old dog, old tricks. Tried but not true. So when I wear my pancho-cloak of invisibility, I imagine you still see me. Why? It glitters like a vampire, the swing of my fringe.

Alex R. Encomienda
CARNALITY

Pogo took one glance out of the window of the bodega and then grimaced. His phone hadn't been charged tonight because he forgot to charge it the night before and he didn't have the money for a cab. It had been raining all night as well.

Just when he was about to chance the storm, his co worker, Mary, walked up from behind him.

"Lousy weather! Want me to drive you home?"

Pogo agreed to go with her but he was obviously nervous. She was considered to be the popular one at work. Pogo was surprised she even bothered to talk to him. She was miles out of his league, he thought.

As they began down the quiet street, Pogo told her his address. Afterwards, he felt compelled to let her know how surprised he was that she decided to drive him home.

"I appreciate you doing this for me. I know I'm not much of a talker at work but you're a good bunch of people. I like to mind my own business. I hope you don't think I'm standoffish."

Mary laughed. "Of course not! I think you're pretty cool. There's no drama with you like with some of the others."

Pogo gave a timid chuckle. "Yeah, I love it that way. Don't you have somewhere to be tonight? It's Friday. Everyone is out partying and socializing."

"I've never been into those things."

Pogo was surprised by her response again. "I'm impressed! A woman with sophistication. I'm just glad you don't think I'm a weirdo."

She chuckled. "You're not weird. And besides, I have a gun in my car. I never let anyone try to hurt me. I'm lucky enough to have never used it but it makes me feel safe having it. My father always told me that there is a feminine intuition when it comes to danger. He told me that his mother would always feel if there was danger around her which prompted her to bring her gun. I believe in my intuition enough to be as careless as I'd like when it comes to others around me."

Pogo agreed. "Great woman she was. What kind of gun is it?"

"Ruger .22."

Pogo was intimidated by her way of thinking and the way she carried herself. He examined her out of the corner of his eye as she drove with one hand on the wheel and the other resting on her lap. She looked well experienced as if she had been independent for quite some time.

"So tell me about yourself… Pogo, right?"

"Yes. And there's not much to tell about me though. I like to keep to myself. I'm a simple person. If I'm not at work, I'm at home in my room."

Mary nodded slowly. "Is that how you like things to be?"

"Yes, it's who I am."

"Who do you live with? And do you have any hobbies?"

"I live with my mom. She's quite old already so I help her out. And I love reading and writing. They're my favorite hobbies."

Mary smiled. "Aw, well that's sweet of you. And literature is a wonderful hobby! The most sincere form of entertainment, I'd say. What's your favorite book?"

"Well, my favorite work isn't even a book. It is a play called *Arcadia*."

"I've read that! The one about determinism, right?"

"Yes, exactly."

"What do you believe in, Pogo?"

He was caught off guard.

"What- as in supernatural forces?"

"No, I mean spiritually or religiously," she replied.

"I'm a Christian man. I've always been one. My mother is also a Christian."

Mary nodded slowly. "Do you believe in determinism?"

"I do believe that everything happens for a reason and that life forces people into each other's lives for a reason but the principles about determinism and the ideology that people are not held responsible for their actions because it wasn't their choice is quite difficult to wrap my head around. It's as if knowing the fact that God is in control gives you an excuse to derail your life. Take stoicism for example; some people think that if they purposely make the decisions that would make their life difficult there would be a reward at the end. This is all my understanding on the matter, by the way."

Mary gave him a double look and then she smiled. He saw her smile and thought that perhaps he might have impressed her with his perspective. His confidence level ascended.

"I believe in determinism but I believe in fate and destiny too. It's hard to believe we don't really have free will. I feel like I can do anything I want but determinism says otherwise."

"Not necessarily; determinism only means that you're doing what you're doing because an even greater force is overseeing your actions and predetermined it to happen without you knowing," Pogo replied.

"So with me giving you a ride home… is that predetermined?" she asked.

"Yes, I think so."

"And everything that happens from this point on is predetermined to happen regardless of what I do as well, right?"

"Sounds about right."

Mary gazed at the empty road ahead and continued to speak, "My mother used to tell me that everyone I meet is for a good reason and that I need to focus on the energy that I get from each encounter. Sometimes, I'll meet someone and then I'll just get these highly negative emotions soon after. She told me that if I spend at least fifteen minutes around someone, I'll be able to feel if there is positive or negative energy from them. Usually, when I feel that there is negative energy, it means that the person has bad intentions. However, if I feel positive energy, they have good, pure intentions. My mother died, but I still believe this to be true. I've used it my whole life and it worked every time. That just confirms that she was right all along."

"What kind of energy do you get from me?"

"Has it been fifteen minutes yet?" she asked.

Pogo glanced at his watch. "It's been twenty."

Mary smiled again, showing her beautiful white teeth. Pogo noticed that she had a dimple on her left cheek but not on her right cheek. She was absolutely angelic, he thought.

"Right now, it's hard to tell for some reason. Give me a few more minutes and I'll be able to tell for sure."

Pogo sat quietly and peered straight ahead at the empty road. The darkness swallowed the entire car and all they were able to see was the glow on each other's faces from the high beams ahead.

"Do you think determinism is a factor when it comes to love?" asked Mary.

Pogo remained quiet for a moment. "I think love is something created between determinism and free will. I mean, we both believe in God. Love comes from God but it is an illusion to an extent. We think love is an entity between us all and it is created in the moments we share but with determinism, it has always been there and it was aligning with the time God created us to perceive. In that regard, I think love is like death. It is inevitable but also predetermined for each of us."

Mary gave him a certain look he'd only imagine seeing from a woman in a film or a magazine. He could not believe that she was looking at him the way she was. Pogo felt as if she was suddenly attracted to him. It gave him a short feeling of confidence and gratification that he never felt before. The fact that his crush looked at him with such an intense and genuine glare suddenly gave him a glimpse of the potential he saw in himself if he had faith in himself throughout these years.

"I know what kind of energy I get from you now."

"What kind?"

"Pure, honest energy, Pogo."

She finally pulled up in front of his house and then turned to smile at him. She noticed him fidgeting though. She looked down and saw his hand moving in the darkness.

As she looked closer, trying to figure out what he was doing, she realized that he was masturbating.

She gasped loudly in fear, panicking to reach beneath her seat.

"But… I thought you wanted to fuck me," he uttered.

At that moment, she pulled out her pistol and shot him in the face at close range. His head slammed against the window and then his body slumped over onto her lap as she quickly drove away.

Sandra Feen
BETWEEN

scope snowscape of spirit
night of your back yard,
cat bells soundless by porch
paws, your steps, enshrined beneath
terrain wintering blue birdhouse, it
tips heavy with second snow,
stark as absence. lean right
a shed, its red prominence
by looming maples
in between

a home: heat of routine
practice makes memory, though
lamps remain erratic.
father sleeps, daughter paces
hallway of vanishing
family.

cat insists touch
urgent, between arms
your tethered hum.

Sandra Feen photos pages 60-61

Laurence Foshee
DOROTHY'S WEDDING NIGHT

Ah bizarre Honeymoon Suite, I'll
try better fitting his rhythms now
that we've hitched. His tenuous vow

to bolster me through trials your
thread count contract forged in rouged drips
of wounded woman. I've seen a

sterner side to him; brooding Bill
took our reins from day one. Yet still

my thoughts are dredged with Regina:
an honor-maid talk (her fingers, lips
fluttered, rounded rife passion for

Portuguese verse) has me drunk; oh how
her *voce* nurtured that name "João!"
"William, we should live in Brazil."

Kelle Grace Gaddis
VISITATIONS

My husband's first visitation was the day after I got the news of his passing. In the dream, his spirit appeared at zero-zero-hundred hours as if following some afterlife military protocol

Feeling haunted was familiar to me. Years before, when my father died in Desert Storm, my mother tied yellow ribbons around the oak trees, put candles in our windows, and raised and lowered our flag each day, dedicated to rituals that demonstrated commitment to husband and country.

I imagined my father as an actor in a movie about war more than as an actual soldier. He became my invention, a peacekeeper even though he was a decorated sniper.

When my father passed, my mother put a picture of him, proud in uniform, next to her bed. "It keeps him close," she said. I nodded, trying to remember one true thing about the man in the frame.

Now, with my husband's body six feet down beneath a flag-draped coffin and his ghost silent at the entrance of our bedroom, a silhouette against a summer moon, I knew I hadn't been a good wife.

No ribbons.

No candles.

No flag.

I brought a lover to his funeral, not that anyone knew except my mother, who noticed how men can't help but track the woman they've slept with.

"What will people think?" my mother asked. I looked away, "We were only married a year. He went to war right after our daughter was born."

But here he was as if I'd kept vigil for him.

We stood before one another like characters in a movie that didn't know their lines. Outside the window, I saw a red Mustang idling on the street *herumph, herumph herumph*. I wanted to run to it, to whatever soldier was inside, and put a thousand comfortable miles between myself and regret.

I was always a vivid dreamer. As a child, I dreamt of uniformed devils. One stands out more than the rest. He was a half-naked black devil with a golden horn. His figure had lumbered past my bedroom, swaying in the darkness, making grumbling noises before tipping his head back and letting out a metallic howl. I hid beneath my sheets until sunrise. When I woke, I remember feeling exhausted and ashamed of my mind's invention.

I have few memories of my childhood. The truest of my father is straightforward. He sent us paychecks; and, when he died, the government continued to send them.

The memories of my mom were more like a song in the distance, one where the melody is familiar, but the words are foreign and inaudible. If she had hopes and dreams, I was unaware of them. The only thing I was fairly certain of was that her public image mattered a great deal to her. Sometimes I would push myself to remember something special but always ended up seeing myself at the edge of her reality, a character without lines, watching the lead while she cleaned house or chatted with men on the phone.

Mother's beautiful. Growing up, I thought she could have stepped off the cover of Military Spouse. She was always perfectly dressed, pressed, and in full make-up. She was a master of appearances and still is.

The next night, I bolted upright and saw him standing at the foot of my bed, his lips moving without sound. My breath raced to my center and held like a tied-off balloon. My heart was pounding. I heard the *herumph, herumph herumph* and knew the red Mustang was out front, black windows obscuring the driver, whose hands I imagined resting on the stick shift and steering wheel while his foot rhythmically pressed the gas pedal.

I was pregnant when I married.

Becoming a military wife wasn't planned. I didn't have a plan, except to be as happy as the people I saw in films.

My spouse and the Mustang returned the next night; this time, he stood at the end of our bed smelling of a men's cologne. I recognized the scent as something a neighbor friend of ours wore. My husband never wore cologne.

I froze.

This time when he spoke, I heard him ask, "Why?'

There is no easy way to explain kisses or the tender touches of another. It's even harder if it's not "another" but others. His friends. When he was deployed for over a year, I was lonely. I wasn't prepared for commitment after growing up with my father's literal absence and my mother's emotional absence. Being a mother weighed on me, whereas being with men made me feel powerful. Except now, caught in a dead man's stare, I wondered if he knew my thoughts.

Our relationship never had a chance. It was snuffed out by absence like a burst of air turning a flame into a twill of smoke. His halfway-around-the-world affection wasn't enough. I needed a body, someone to watch over me, someone to protect me from the devils I knew.

When I brought a lover into our home for the first time, my husband was all I thought about. I imagined his handsome face behind dark glasses, his body over a sandbag aiming at some unknown enemy. I knew my actions would cut him to the core, cause him to question his worth, but I didn't stop. I reasoned he'd never know, even though I knew his friend's faces could reveal our secrets in an instant.

My husband appeared, again and again, always getting closer. He'd sat at the end of the bed and then on the side of it. Tonight he's lying next to me, holding my hand. He never said another word. After a week, I could look him in the eye. Tonight I can't stop talking.

"You left me-"

Without reply, he rolled towards me and kissed my cheek.

"I needed you-"

"I'm sorry I hurt you-"

And, just like that, he was gone. The air felt cooler. The curtain moved as if caught by a breeze. Beyond it, the glass was foggy with condensation. The floor felt like it gave way beneath me. I fell until I woke.

The day after the last dream of my husband, my mother came to visit.

We stood over my child's crib. She asked, "How are you getting along on your own?" My heart rose in my chest and, although still morning, I sensed the Mustang's herumph, herumph herumph in the drive. I took a breath and said, "Terribly, he came to me in my dreams."

My mother's forever faraway eyes met mine, but instead of being distant, she appeared fully present. She took my hand and said, "I know what that's like."

The configuration of my memory fell away. I saw my mother on all fours scrubbing the kitchen floor until it shined. When she looked up and saw me, my four-year-old self, peaking at her work, she'd sat back on her heels and scooped a handful of suds from a fresh bucket and hid it behind her back. She'd lifted her other hand and beckoned with one finger. She pulled the suds from behind her back and blew white bubbles into the air that fell like snow. We'd laughed, scooping suds from the bucket and blowing them all around until the kitchen was a mess. It was the first positive memory of my childhood I recalled of the two of us together.

I squeezed my mother's hand, and she squeezed mine back.

Mom began visiting more often, and more memories came.

Pancakes with blueberry smiley faces.

Watching my mother teach my daughter to tie her shoes brought back the memory of her teaching me, "Bunny ears, Bunny ears, playing by a tree. See little Bunny criss-cross the tree, trying to catch me. Bunny ears, Bunny ears, jump in the hole. Watch little Bunny come out the other side beautiful and bold."

Shaswata Gangopadhyay
POETRY OF THIRD WORLD

I am nobody, nobody at all
Just a cultivator of cotton belonging to third world,
His youngest son
I have grown up by swallowing the froth of sea,
On my burnt skin
There is printed the world-map all over the body

Hunger rises in spiral motion
Around my stomach

If you give me love, I'll multiply it three times
By sheer magic
And put it under your feet
If you give me hatred, if you offend me
From my top to bottom
I'll come back not to take revenge
But to my writing papers
And I will throw each of my poems,one after another
Just like daggers

Yes, all the boys of third world are just like this

Suchismita Ghoshal
I AM A SAVIOUR IN A PARALLEL WORLD

And one day I won't wake up from the languid
sleep of this euphoric world anymore,
my dreams will take me to a parallel world
where I am given all the superpowers.
I have the power to omit all the vices,
I have the power to prevent disasters and natural calamity,
I have the power to remove the sufferings of mankind,
I have the power to erase the struggles of nature,
I have the power to make blood mongers relinquish on wars,
I have the power to snatch the struggles and traumas of children,
I have the power to insert the taste of literature again,
I have the power to set an example of companionship,
I have the power to uplift women to sing the unsung lullabies of
empowerment,
I have the power to swish the demons of betrayal and lust,
I have the power to save the unconditional love,
I have the set the equilibrium of poor and rich,
I have the power to stop religious fights,
I have the power to let people understand the purity,
I have the power to disappear all the diseases,
I have the power to make people see the beauty of blessing through its
evanescence,
I have the power to right every wrong,
I have the power to throng all the positivity
and every power that sets the world in the right place.
And one day, I won't wake up from the languid
sleep of this euphoric world anymore and witness myself ready on a
journey of a savior for this earthly world.

Robert Gibbons
NEGRO SUNSHINE

I am a ward of state

a perpendicular peninsular birth me created from Orlando craters and
muck raiders.

We all came from somewhere, grandma said, "Georgia," but it could
have been South Carolina; who knows when you migrate, walk late
in red clay Tallahassee, in the cay of Okeechobee

Negro sunshine, giver of two dollars

and a trash dump, will make fish and grits with lumps of clay; the hands

change the water to wine folk said, you will be just fine
if you live right, if you treat people right

a fight for equality, on the board and in society, put the effort forth
without impunity, who knows what will rise up out of the mess of a
plantation
collard greens and a peck of beans pig slop of the auction block
but there are survivals, if not liable

to a people that want more, a charge and a keep, a hope and a speak
a ward of her state of her consciousness

money did not come easy when you take in the wash, hang clothes for
a living
a primer to an education, and dare

to educate, sunshine state, mate

to a destiny, let me be free to read, so that I can set up a homestead,

sunshine, blinding glare, sanfoka

in red ochre, southern pink, may -green and a touch of Carolina
vermillion, who said moss does not have beauty, it is just a duty to be
free.

Michael Guinn
ON MY KNEES

I've decided that
The next time i ask that special someone to marry me
I'm getting down on both knees.
Because the last time
One knee wasn't enough.
So this time I getting down on both knees because i know thats a
position where God hears me speak the loudest.
This time while on both knees I'm praying that the God in her
connects to the God in me.

Because i'm tired of running these emotional streets.
Tired of cold sheets, frozen meats.
I'm ready to give all of me.
Tired having the soul of a poet whose words got lost on the way to gm
the page.
And even though God is the King of my spirit she is the Queen of my
soul. Ya see she will be the genesis in the book of me. And I just wanna
go back and rewrite past chapters so that i can be her ever after.

And now that this wedding proposal is complete. Now that I'm ready
to run into tomorrow with the love of my life. She's... she's gonna have
to help me up because well i've got bad knees.

Dr. Tom C. Hunley
QUESTIONS FOR FURTHER STUDY

1) How are these poems like dark dad jokes with Gillette® razors in them and wild slept-on hair and a receding hairline all the punchlines lost like a wedding ring swallowed by a toddler sitting on a potty chair learning that *this is going to hurt us more than it hurts you* is just one of life's pretty lies like the one about birdsong and poetry both being peaceful and chime-like when really both are elaborate ways of saying *let's get it on* or *stay out of my tree*?

2) Is it possible to write something original about turning fifty what would Keats have written about turning fifty had he turned fifty will my name be written on ice with spray paint or carved into a tree next to my wife's name or whispered into our grandkids' ears soft as snow falling on the wings of a dead bird?

3) What is the symbolism of the light in the puddle the Buffalo-shaped ache the soap bubble the skipping stone and if the author were truly a good father would he for real compare his kids to Bigfoot and Napoleon or write poems like flashlights shining in their eyes?

4) Have you or anyone you know made it through *Remembrances Of Things Past* have you felt the loss of someone you never really knew have you seen through the color blue into its constituents magenta and cyan have you felt like there's something wrong with you but you never knew what until you read about it in a book and if so did you hate the book and its author or did you feel grateful like the time you were about to sing "The Star Spangled Banner" before a baseball game with a big piece of toilet paper clinging to your shoe when a bat boy jogged up to you, pointed out the toilet paper, pulled it off you, and disposed of it in the dugout?

5) Do these poems move across your heart a) like tumbleweeds across a desert b) like wind gusts blown in from the sea or c)

like the beautiful new person at work who gets promoted
before learning your name?

6)   Where children are concerned is it fair to say that the heart is
Santa's sleigh weighed down by an impossible load the heart a
small thing dragged across the night by large animals?

7)   Is adopting a scared teenager more like trying to garden on a
scarred battlefield or like insisting on the day-olds at Dunkin
Donuts is it like rescuing meat from a grinder in some kind of
PETA-inspired intervention and then trying with all you have
not to become the meat not to become the grinder?

8)   Is autism the beginning of a new stage of consciousness what
would you say to the loneliest whale in the world if he could
hear or understand you if you could hear his lonely 52-Hertz
cry just lower than the lowest note on a tuba inaudible even to
other whales?

9)   Is it possible to die from a broken heart to dream yourself
into a better self to have an allergic reaction to water what is the
probability of being born one in 400 trillion according to some
guy on the Internet wow here we are somehow here IRL and
on the WWW how does anyone ever yawn and why can't we all
live every moment in awe like Adam at the moment when he
first saw Eve or like the first Cro-Magnon to gaze at a
constellation and paint it on the cave wall?

pj johnson Poet Laureate of the Yukon
IT WAS THE LAND

"A recent poem written as I and my fellow Canadians struggled to come to terms with the discovery of unmarked graves on the grounds of residential schools in Canada. In honour of the many children who never returned home, the poem is called "it was the land".

no one knew the evil men could do
behind closed doors
no one spoke of it
no one said sorry
and in the end
it was the land
the very land itself
that spoke

it was the land
that carried the secrets
that knew the truth
that yielded a million sorrows
that stopped us like a thunderbolt
in the streets.
god forgive us
the whispers were true

it was the land that spoke for thousands
denied a life. denied a family
denied a mother tongue
and as our grief-filled days
stretched out before us
like a blanket of fear
from the land of the Mi'kmaq to *Haida* Gwaii
we were numb with disbelief

75

for it was the land
the very land itself
that spoke to us in the darkness
in the sacred smoke of our ancestors
and in the voices of our children
who whispered on the wind
guiding us
showing us the way

telling us
there will be a time
for coming together
as a nation. as a people. and as a family
to celebrate now
and lift our brothers and sisters
as never before
our tears are never far from the surface

it always gets darker before the light comes back

Ken Jones
THE POET (For All of Us)

The Poet rises up each day
Writes to take the fear away
That tomorrow he might not write
Or have the strength to fight.
His words come from his holy soul
They seek to make people whole
Or at least to have them stop and think
How we're all chained in this link
Of human feelings and raw needs
His heart of love often bleeds.
But if one person hears his thoughts
He knows his efforts weren't for naught
So today I thank you all who read
These simple thoughts my spirit breeds....

Climate Change Collage by Ken Jones

Sean Arthur Joyce
from ***DIARY OF A PANDEMIC YEAR***
12. PLAGUE OF WORMS

As weather in Western Canada continues unseasonably cool and wet during June, gardeners are beset by infestations of leaf rollers attacking fruit trees.

"All that is very well, but let us cultivate our garden."
—Voltaire, *Candide*

Pale green question marks, they descend
on silk skylines—pure appetite,
unstoppable as raindrops. Leaves curl
inward, as if seared by a torch.

The sky furrows its brow—annoyed,
edgy. Through the air the news comes—
an adrenaline wind, a sick stomach,
sharp smell of cortisol in a panicked herd.

Driven indoors and driven apart,
worms infest the brain, turning
and mining the soil. Summer light
is beaten, flat as moth muslin.

Highways convulse, rage unspooling
global meridians, the psyche's
paratroopers. Here in this garden,
I draw my boundary, a backyard Moses

79

with no flock to save. Back bent, fingers

in moist earth, a pinch of plant food,

a slop of water so roots can drink,

satisfy the thirst of cells to divide, multiply,

and capture the sun in chlorophyll sails.

Irtika Kazi
STORMBOUND

Last two days trudged by—
Fixing taps overflooding the apartment.
Father finds another way to keep himself
employed.
Days, like, clumsy enjambments,
Untethered by the gray stillness of hurricanes.
He bottles up emotions from where they leak.
There is power and courage in staying when
One has the choice to leave.
Father sees the possibility of a paradise blooming
Atop the bones of his labor—
Like Michelangelo's creation of Adam
I witnessed from the ceiling of Sistine Chapel,
Half sculpted.
The winds do not cease,
Ricocheting around him; embracing
His woes like monks in ardent worship;

Then he is gone

Brian Kehinde
"TENESMIC (APPROACHING THE ARC)"

    somewhere in the dark thoughts forming
dark clouds behind my skull
it is as it should be
cogito, ergo sum
       true intentions buried beneath my skin
     i feel preconditioned
to being contrite and praying daily
resigned to being lonely
perhaps i am as i should be
       for every compulsion, action, thought, emotion
i misinterpret as wrong
  or worse, as criminal
why not? it's what you've taught me
that these hands do both good and evil in equal measure
i think you are the enemy
in your ignorance, you fall for insincerity
you make me not want to know what i know
about the nature of humanity
scarlet letter scapegoat
a uniformly jaundiced coat
in tragedies typical, predictable
seeds of tradition planted
permissive resentments
childhood's end, not welcome
zip me up in the adult straightjacket
which way to the fitting room, gentlemen?
      no rationalities generated
  no resolutions guaranteed
a filthy fucked up world i'm in
all becoming clear to me
a filthy fucked up world i'm in
how can i scrub it off? get clean?
  another mask worn called happy-go-lucky
a go along to get along scheme
  a mental coping mechanism
  a brain's default routine
but my embryonic arc of light
dying, growing dimmer by the second

how many words exist for sadness?
how many phrases describe depression?
melancholy, bittersweet, dour, pensive
heavyhearted, mournful, doleful, shitty
the wisdom old age and pessimism brings
    intuition gone missing, unrelatable
senses dulled, dehumanized
i am indebted and indentured with no desires
relentlessly out of touch
temptingly out of reach
    solid ground adrift, permanence marooned
my knees curled up beneath me
    expecting the worst, never asking to be born
allow my impulsion to break through noise
break through stillness
if only for just a millionth of a second
if only for just once
can God tell me why tears and crying taste
so goddamn good sometimes?
days upon days that prey upon me
make me antsy
make me act out erratically
chasing poetic ideals into tunnels that dead end
that shove me into a padded room
with no windows, no illuminations
sick to death of this ostentatious stoic front
i keep and i watch
my sleepless solemn throb
my disassociation nods
my thoughts imprisoned by the dark
my dreams suffering from malnutrition

& what a maudlin character i must seem to most of you
so self-absorbed, i need an audience for it
an artist starved for what i deserve and choose
a romance of the miserable outcast
a hunchback in love with my own pain
a bellybutton-lint picking bastard
that bequeaths himself to the infinite stars
an insufferable premadonna cringe
playing the world's last good nerve
on the strings of a tiny violin.

Art by Wolf Man

Paul Konieki
CODE TWITCHING

Yoking
was to now
an initiate of the disciples

of the less obscure
inquires
has this light

already passed?
What the lens
won't tell

as we snatch
sun-death
and hide it in our phones

is whose release
whose pardoning
whose definition

of escape-hatch
God-hunger
dereliction and radix

is the taproot here?
In the distance
an undertaker stork

has the horizon in it's bill.
Not the beast of some
who hound

love like an answer
but the first small thing
that hid

by building space on space
wider than silence
and silence's desires

as the world drowns
in a mouth
filled with suet and down.

Above tonight
the stars on loan
are an abandonment

of eyes
Mars and Venus sluicing
the blue-black latticework

praying for all
who remain unnamed
a bit of soul

blenching each new breath
cold skeletons ready
as a dark god wakes

farther and farther
away. Silence tastes of iron
and soon.

Dressed by touch and feel
the sky holds fast
to gravity and turning

like goings on
going on to the vanishing point
might mean something.

The last sortie to freedom
is captain-less and fell.
Silence, our disaster.

Life is hunger and bombs.
The universe is expanding because
God is a tired parent hiding.

I am a tamasha.
I am a tangent of commotions.
I am a marabou

in three forms
mystical, aggressive,
and distracted.

Look, things flying in the air.
Click, click, click.
Save to photos. Forward. Share.

Where the spirit and the body
divest
leave me uncontrol

warm belly of butterfly blood full
inexorable loneliness
and code twitching

the queasiness of final light
setting all about
is you

last ray
before the universe implodes back
into a red legume

before you taught
me how to make
your favorite soup.

In the rear view mirror
on the hard-road
of my pupil's depthless

enigmatic lake
four words float.
Nothing will touch me

Art by Wolf Man

W. Ruth Kozak

THE MIGHTY PEN

"A pen is certainly an excellent instrument to fix a man's attention and to inflame his ambition."
John Adams (diary entry Nov. 14, 1760)

WRITE'S RULE #1: *Always carry a notebook and pen with you to jot down those brilliant plot ideas, scintillating dialogue and scraps of narrative that come to you while you sip coffee at Starbucks or ride the bus to work.*

These spontaneous thoughts are the pure stream-of-consciousness bits that will keep your writing bright and alive. Don't wait until you get home, or you'll have forgotten them. Keep a pen and paper by your bed too. Some fine thoughts may come to you just as you're drifting off and if you wait until morning they'll be lost in your dream-world.

WRITER'S RULE #2: *Learn to type, because you'll be spending half your lifetime at a keyboard. More importantly, editors will not accept handwritten manuscripts.*

I still have a box filled with hand-written stories in notebooks along with my own illustrations from when I was twelve, and seriously considering a writing career. One of the things I wanted more than anything in the world was a typewriter. A real typewriter like reporters used. I was convinced my parents would get me one.

Alas! When Christmas came, I was presented with a small festively wrapped box. Perhaps the typewriter was hidden somewhere in the closet or on the porch? No such luck! Inside the box was a Bulova wrist watch with an expandable gold strap. I was crushed with disappointment.

"It's a beautiful watch," my Mother said. I knew she meant well. I was a kid who always daydreamed and dawdled, perpetually late for appointments and school. And now I'd had no excuse not to get home by my 9 o'clock curfew. But I couldn't be convinced that a wrist watch was a better, more practical a gift, than a typewriter.

It wasn't until my fourteenth birthday that I got my wish. A second-hand black Underwood. A real typewriter like reporters use in editorial news rooms. I spent hours in the solitude of my bedroom pounding the keys, writing pages and pages of words. By the time I was sixteen I'd churned out half a dozen short novels all with a historical theme.

When I went to live in Greece in the '80's I bought myself a bright red portable Brother. I had no furniture so used an upturned drawer for a table and spent hours typing travel stories. Every story I marketed, typed on that little Brother, was published. I've kept it as a memento of those days, when the travel journalist was born.

WRITER'S RULE #3 : *Learn to write with new technology, but don't give up your pen!*

Eventually technology caught up with me and I graduated to a word processor. How wonderful to not have to retype pages, change ribbons -- to be able to spell-check and correct, cut and paste. No more clack-clack ding of the old typewriter. Now just a soft click click of the computer keys.

One summer when I went back to Greece to travel and write, I bought myself a palm pilot and small fold-up keyboard. As I am often camping, this was a perfect tool for me, portable and compact and more practical than a lap-top. I wrote all summer composing, editing, taking notes.

When I returned home I became caught up in moving to a new apartment, taking my possessions out of storage, setting up. By the time I got back to writing again and went to hot-sync my summer's work into the word processor, the palm's battery had run down (I had forgotten to read the fine print that said to keep it plugged in and charging). All my work had vanished! Fortunately, the mighty pen came to the rescue. I'd hand-written some of the notes and had saved them. Otherwise all would have been lost!

WRITER'S RULE #4 : *Familiarize yourself with modern technology! But don't give up your pen! The pen will connect you with the page, the quality of thoughts, those important words that you don't want to lose!*

I didn't get my first computer until late in the 90's when I was asked to write some information for a travel book. I still usually always keep notes, and my first drafts are generally written by hand first. I believe that the pen is more trustworthy than technology. In fact, this is the second attempt at writing this blog. The first one I wrote vanished into cyberspace when I accidentally tapped the wrong key. All I had of the original were a few hand-written notes. The mighty pen had made its point!

"And, as imagination bodies forth
The forms of things unknown, the poet's pen
Turns them to shapes, and gives to airy nothing
A local habitation and a name."
Shakespeare (*"A Midsummer Night's Dream"*)

Gopal Lahiri
DESIGN

Plants are everywhere, and there are poems
on the wall- more serene than sheets of ice,
with a heavy dose of organic interior.

Aroma of freshly ground coffee wafts in
the one sentence song is drowned out,
one eyed bird is flapping on the window sill.

Long scar that I smooth away with deft punctuations,
comes back with four large white tombs,
bending to receive elegies and ethos,

The marble floor outshines the whites of the clouds,
shadows knife the steep staircase,
a painting that lulls me, but hold you tight.

You search around, all those accidental glances,
I am trying to design my universe of green grass.

Gabrielle Langley
BLACK LEOPARD

A jungle in Myanmar,
tangle of vines,
trees
blocking light,
mosquitoes hovering
in green shadow.
Melanism,
when shades
of blue and violet
turn the dark
a deeper black.

You as prey,
spellbound,
trapped,
in crosshairs,
the eyes, two citrines
polished,
the thin edge
of a pink-red tongue,
curling
like the petal
of some obscene flower
flickering in a frame
of yellow fangs.

Licking his lips
a few hours later,
the tycoon-hunter
sitting in front
of a campfire,
pot-bellied,
surrounded by servants,
caught
red-handed
fingering the pelt
of a rare female
black leopard,

an exotic soup
made from her flesh,
the poacher
detained,
temporarily
the money, a bribe,
the slow peristalsis,
the meat
worming its way
through intestine.

Stacey Lawrence
SHADOWS

Your easel
still slants here
overlooks our pond
roiled with mud
tubes of used blues left scattered
in damp weeds
bleed into earth
where it seems you
crouch on a sailcloth stool
gliding a badger's bristles
over canvas.

Stacey Lawrence
FRONTLINE

The jar says
tips for girls, the girls
are old,
round, Russian
deep croaky throats,
Borscht with sour

cream poured into
fitted jeans
gems mounted on
rear pockets,
hunched over worn countertops
they fling beads of sweat with

dingy sleeves
and sweep butter across
bagels for minimum wage,
August in Jersey,
both ovens blasting.

Penitent, I drop
in 10 dollars
she grants me a nod
as her colleague gifts me
a present,
wrapped in parchment.

The man who was afraid of
LOVE

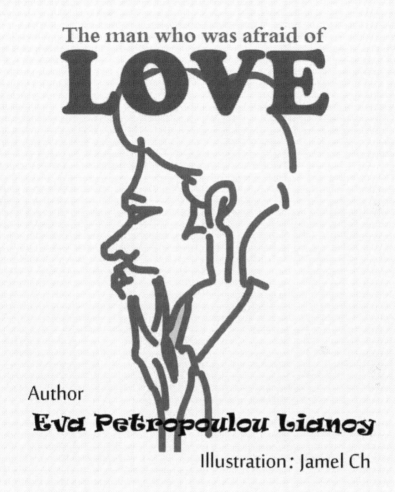

Author
Eva Petropoulou Lianoy

Illustration: Jamel Ch

Eva Petropoulous Lianoy
THE MAN WHO WAS AFRAID OF LOVE

Once upon a time, in a village near the forest, was living a man, very dark hair and with a deep regard.

He was living alone in a wooden house. He was making everything with his bare hands.

Every day he was walking up before the sun rise and he went deep into the forest, he was picking the most high tree and start working from day to night. All the furniture even the plate, the spoon and the fork was made by wood.

The man did not have a lot of friends, or neighbors, and the closest home was miles and miles away. He never married and he spent of his life working the wood. His work makes him famous in the near village and they come to him and ask him to repair everything it was broken. And the man gave all his time and attention to the wood and it was like they understand each other, the wood was taken life and become a beautiful table, a beautiful chair, a very nice door.

People they were start to come from a big city and asking for more furniture and other decorations.

One day he was preparing a wooden chair, and he was out in the open air, when suddenly a rare perfume comes to him. He looked around but nobody was with him. So, the man continue to work the chair and try to give a nice shape and wanted to put also some beautiful colours...

Again the perfume makes him turn his head and then he noticed down to the earth, a very beautiful strange flower with several colours...

"I do not remember see this flower before" he said.

"No, you don't. Because I was a seed and some days ago a sparrow bring him here from a foreign country. But as the sparrow got tired from the long journey, he hide me in the earth, and he thought that he can come

98

and eat me later.... But he forgot. I am a seed and if u burry me I will grow up and become a... "

"A beautiful flower that smells so nice" he said the carpenter.

"Yes, but I smell like that, only if I am happy..

Some minutes ago an ant passed and we spoke about the news, he gave me news about my other family, so I m more happy.."

The perfume was exceptional. It was like the perfume of the orange flowers and some of ylang ylang. The man had never thought he could spoke with a flower.

"I must finish my chair I have a lot do. I must finish before night come. " said the carpenter and start again to work on the chair.

"Why are you so hurrying to finish your chair?   I see nobody else here with you. Do you have family, a wife or children?"
Asked the flower

"No, I am alone and I am very busy. So do not ask me silly questions, I must work because I have a chair to deliver...."

"How is possible to work in such a beautiful day, look up the sky is so blue, look the forest and the trees, such a beautiful picture." said the flower, and continued " I need some fresh water and if you have some more grass, you can bring it, close to me, so I will have company. "

The carpenter start to scratch his head and then he said," for such a small thing, u have many requests. I tell you that I am busy. I have to finish my work, at must deliver the chair to my client. "

So the man started to work on his wooden chair and did not listen to the complaints of the flower, that it suddenly became more and more curious.

"Have you ever love someone?" Asked the flower.

"What? What kind of silly question is that?" A
Asked the carpenter really angry.

" I will respond to this for you. U never loved anyone or anything or I think, you don't even love yourself... ", said the flower and turn his petals to the sun

"I feel much better, but I really need some water.." repeat again the flower

"Ohh OK. I will go to bring you some water."

The man left and went to the house, he took a big vase and he put some water. Then he went out and he threw the water to the flower.

"Ohhhh you almost destroy my little petals. I tell you, you really never love anything or anyone. You just threw the water, with all your forces. You must be gentle with my petals.
You care a rose around the sand ..."

The flower explain for hours the way the carpenter must give him water, and that he must time to time change and put some soil, and ask the carpenter, if he can find some other seeds, and put them close to him, so he will not feel alone.

Then carpenter had a better idea, to take a big pottery, he put some soil inside and he suggested to his friend, the flower to plant it in there so he will not be alone anymore.

They will be together as the carpenter; he was strong enough to carry out, the pottery with his friend, even when he went to the big city for buying new tools.

After months have passed the carpenter was so attached to his flower that he started to read books about gardening and every day tried to make his friend happier.

He bought a new pottery and he placed it near the window so his flower could have a sun bath all day. When he went to the forest for cutting woods for his work, he had created a small wooden car and he put there the pottery, so they were always together.

They spoke a lot about everyday life and sometimes for the future. But the flower always said that, we must show our love now, not in future".

Today is so important for us the flowers, from the first sunshine will catch us, we must take as much light we can, and drink water, and have someone to care for us, as we are so fragile. The flower was growing up and become so beautiful. And his perfume also becomes so popular, and when neighbors visited the carpenter, they will ask for the name of this flower, so they can also find the seeds and plant to their garden.

The carpenter told to his neighbors, "My flower is very rare and I do not know if you will find the same seeds. I named my flower "Love". But as this flower has a deep impact on my life, I give him this name. Because he help me understand that today is more important than the future.

And love is a free energy and more we give away,
more is coming back to us. "

The carpenter and the flower stay friends for a long time. And the carpenter always left some hours free after his work, for gardening as he get so many secrets from his friend, that he could grow any strange seed and make it a strong tree.

His garden was very famous and people come from all over the country.

And when someone ask him about his secret of this beautiful garden. The carpenter respond, with a smile:

"Love, is the secret."

The End

Flower watercolor by Dustin Pickering

"Collaboration" by Angie Mack

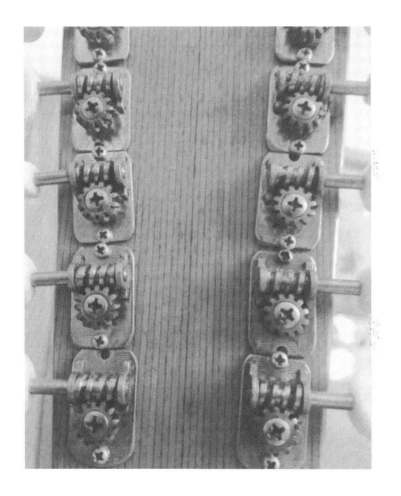

Angie Mack
VIBRATIONS*

The quake
The jolt
The vibe

The drums
They do
REVIVE

The beat
The bang
The bump

Collaboration.
Not just one.

Shake
Shimmer
Jazz!

Tap.
Massage.
Those hands!

Rock and rattle.
Rattle the cold.
Friction.
Together.
Hotter
when old.

Buzz
and
Wiggle

Giggle
she
Does

Music and dancing
Vibrations of love

Body quakes
Muscles faint
Heart it aches
For more.

Roller coasters.
Runways.

Race cars
and machines.

Rumble
Roar

I'm out the door

*punctuation intentional

angiemackreilly

Mantri Pragada Markandeyulu
BRIDE'S AGONY

With this self-advocacy and self-consoling able to settle-down after
some time Able to manage crucial moment & time.... read more

I knew it well
Things do not favour me
It was a life and death question.
I hoped for good //

I was always praying the Almighty
To clinch the marriage issue
I like no untoward incidents
I was little bit apprehensive //

Doubted my ensuing in-laws
I was observing their psychology
Time was rolling out
I was in full control with deep thoughts //

I was looking at my wrist watch
Observing the Time & date
I was disappointed for few days
I thought for a while //
To swim in the Life Sea
To reach the Life Shore //

I like to swim in the Sea
To reach the Sea Shore //

I thought, never to give up
Hopes always live with hopes
I had a detailed discussion
I had exciting talk //
I was relieved from tension
I asked uncle
Sought for marriage alliance with Uncle's son
I want to settle in life //

Run the family with peace of mind
Hubby has better principles in life
I recouped with heavy breath
Prepared for countdown days //

I made gate dash for clinching my issue
Observed bridegroom's father carefully
He walked to the door
I knew, time was running out //

Suppressed the urge to check my watch
I took a deep breath
Started counting in reverse under my breath
Like, ten, nine, eight, seven, six to zero //

Though perturbed, kept my mind balanced
Came to the sense
Requested for a glass of water
Settled down for few seconds to ease tension //

My heavy breath has calmed down
Had sigh of relief
My inner sense told me to observe the wrist watch
Watching the psychology of boy's parents //

The inner 'sacred soul' told me to speak very softly and politely
Prepared for any eventuality in this crucial issue
Consoling my heavy inner heart
Trying to cool down my brain //

I was able to pacify myself
Able to remember my friends telling me that –
After the storm, there is always calm
After the sunshine there are showers of rain //

With this self-advocacy and self-consoling
Able to settle-down after some time
Able to manage crucial moment & time
Urged Aunty and Uncle to perform this marriage soon //

Would be mother-in-law understood well
The agony of Bride was well received

Would be bride has been given good treatment
Well spoke by would be in-laws.//

Would be in-laws agreed in toto
The bride was given an assurance by in-laws
The engagement would be accepted
The Marriage would be performed soon.//

With this kind words of in-laws
The bride was happy
Bridegroom was also happy
Engagement and Marriage took place.//

Both the new couples Happy
Both the In-laws Happy
Oh the marriage day, invitee blessings showered
New couples were very happy.//

Went on Honeymoon like twitter-shelter
'Young couples Twitter Shelter Home
Looks like Great Princes - Bonding with Loving Heart
Universal Beauty-Smarty in the World
Bonding Hands Forever, Life partners soon //

Later, Fly Away like Twitter, for Honeymoon Joy
Settle in Life for a Big Show Soon //

Mike Matthews
WE ARE THE SAME BIRDS

In the evening's mysterious smile,
he placed two clear glasses on his stoop
next to the front door.

He filled them equally with pure,
filtered water that held the light
of the sunset like perfect diamond eyes.

In one, he dropped
a single, dark pebble,
pupil-black.

Then, he turned his back,
spinning easily on his heels
and on the balls of his feet,
paused and tilted his head,
and he closed the door—
its hinges sung the song of a dove.

That night, he dreamed
of pink fire, white arms
of blue stars reaching
like children wanting to hug.

His dreams popped and bloomed—
they kicked up powerfully turbulent
thunderstorms of dust and hammering rocks
squeezing one another tightly
until their tears settled to great, calm pools.

In the morning, he waited in silence
before he touched the doorknob.
The turning latch of the door
slid with the sibilance of a newborn's
sleeping breath.

He stepped out of his front door
and looked at his experiment.

His eyes grew wide and perplexed,
brows coming together like the bent rim
of a warped hat brim.

The two water glasses sat where he'd left them,
yet both were filled with black, round marbles
as if mirrors had been set between them,
and between the mirrors, marble black birds.

The writhing black dots of a single mass of birds,
undulant, pressed by the invisible pulsing palms
of wind currents as if kneaded, acting like a thing
that is not a thing but a unified bunch of single,
black, unarticulated birds held together for a moment
by an idea—

    We are birds—
    We are the same birds.

For a moment alone in the floating
air-currents, until there was a kind
of aeronautic cellular division,
a rising organism split, divided,
and calmly seething subsided,
still and spherical like a galaxy of black stars
unaffected by any nightmares.

Digital artwork "Ashes" page 112 by Mike Matthews from the forthcoming collection
by the same name

Donella McLean
THE OCEAN

Krill filled pillows of
Water shifts forward
Deep waves of current
Brine scented air
Flux backwards then
Forward into the tide
Make friends with the
Offing.

Donella McLean
POETRY

Words are my vehicle
Rhyme my method
Verse my duty
Composition my constitution
You are my muse
But lyric my song
Rhythm my singular notion
Epic is my words
And that's just the first stanza

Mysti Milwee
OSIYO, OFF-ROAD DREAMS

Between the audacious valley's
baby fawns graze in the morning dew
before the thirteen days of rain
to drown out the shadows between the meadows

Where the leaves hung after a long summer's rain:
Sloping gestures, flow through
an aura of hallelujah,
in the half-light of dreams being awakened

Osiyo, brave sun cascading down mountain tops
to touch, purple flowers
waving *Osiyo*, to dancing dandelions
along the path of fragmented rocks

that built off-road dreams, where the light beams
where hope heals broken roads,
and peace where the chaos once was,
leaving hearts to transcend in incandescent light

in an after-glow of provision, but yet a vision
that life exists on the off-road, a way to honor
and accept what was lost and found.
To trust ourselves, even when dreams met reality.

*Notation: *Osiyo*, means 'hello' in Cherokee.

Richard Modiano
FIRST THOUGHT, BEST THOUGHT

The expression "first thought, best thought" is usually attributed to Allen Ginsberg. Ginsberg indeed popularized the phrase but it was actually coined by his Buddhist teacher Chogyam Trungpa Rinpoche. Further, there is William Blake's dictum "First Thought is Best in Art, Second in Other Matters" also cited by Ginsberg. This expression is often misunderstood to mean first word, best word by people who believe that thoughts and words are one and the same.

Behind first thought, best thought stands a particular epistemology. It's based on a specific practice of observing the rise and fall of thoughts as they occur moment by moment, called by Buddhists *shamatha-vipashana* in some traditions and *zazen* in others.

The careful and repeated observation that comes from being grounded in *shamatha-vipashana* practice will reveal that thoughts are not simply words but images and emotions, so to capture that first thought is to be aware of the image/emotion in all its starkness. The skill comes in finding the right words to embody that thought in its naked immediacy, and this may involve re-writing.

I say re-writing instead of revision because the latter term implies a departure from that first thought/vision. When looked at a second time, re-vised, re-viewed, either a self-censoring curtain drops between the poet and her original inspiration or the energy of the first flash has been dissipated. Then the poem becomes words referring to earlier words so that the first energizing thought is lost and the end product at its best becomes a prism of language through which language itself is viewed, and at its worst becomes a dried ball of word paste.

"If you stick with the first flashes, then you're all right. But the problem is, how do you get to that first thought – that's always the problem. The first thought is always the great elevated, cosmic, non-cosmic *shunyata* thought. And then, at least according to the Buddhist formulation, after that you begin imposing names and forms and all that. So it's a question of catching yourself at your first open thought" Ginsberg noted. The unfamiliar word *shunyata* is a Sanskrit term that's usually translated as "emptiness" and refers to the insubstantial nature of thoughts and things.

The method of composition using first thought, best thought is noting the image/emotion in words as soon as it manifests itself in one's mind, "like a flash of lightening in the dark of night." The poet attempts to describe in words the thought in all its vivid particulars. Sometimes the poet hits the right words immediately, sometimes the poet must carve the poem out of all the words and images that pour from her pen (or word processor.) Gregory Corso called this process "tailoring." The poet takes the fabric bolt of words and cuts it to an elegant suit of language that preserves original mind in all its rich allusiveness, charged with emotion and insight.

So first thought, best thought is a challenge to the poet who wants to communicate that super-charged flash of awareness-insight into the reality of the moment, whatever that moment may be, however it may be characterized, whether of joy or sorrow, awe or despair, or quiet appreciation of what is.

Tina Wittendorff Mortensen
EXCERPT FROM *THE AMULET OF THE LAST EARTH GHOSTS*

Year 884

The wind was howling outside the wooden shutters of our windows. It was getting dark, but my brother still hadn't returned. I'd told him to be back before midnight. The elders had warned us against leaving the house when there was a full moon. It was the night of the wolves, but those weren't the ones you should fear. No, the wolves would keep to themselves, but they'd attract the ghosts. Some said that the wolves' howling woke the ghosts from the dead, others that the wolves only howled because they were afraid of these creatures in the woods. Only one thing was certain: Every time there had been a full moon, you'd find dead wolves under the trees in the woods the next day. My brother didn't fear the wolves, and he didn't believe in ghosts, either. He had gone off to visit the widow that lived in a nearby village. He had a soft spot for her. Of course, she was both young and beautiful, and her husband's accident had been a tragedy, but it had been my brother's luck. I was sure she wouldn't be a widow much longer.

I had to find my brother before it was too late. He'd never stayed the night with this woman. After all, he was an honest man. He'd never sinned in his life. No, he wouldn't stay the night until they were married. You'd never know what could have happened. Maybe his horse had gotten hurt and he had to walk home through the woods. I couldn't let that happen. He'd never stayed out this late before. I got my cloak and went to the stable to saddle the horse. If I hurried, I'd be able to get my brother home before midnight.

The night was cold and foggy. The summer was fading. The wolves' howling had already begun, and their cries got louder and louder as I got closer to the woods. My horse suddenly stopped as if it could sense something ahead of us. I encouraged it to keep going, but it wouldn't move. I got down from the saddle and tried to drag the horse along with me, but instead, the horse reared, and I was thrown to the ground.

"Easy, boy!" I called out, but it was too late.

The horse had already turned around and was on its way back to the stable. I should have gone home, too, but I was already so close to the woods. I'd only have to walk a few more miles before the widow's village would be in sight. I couldn't turn back now. I got up from the ground, brushed the dirt off my cloak, and rushed toward the woods. I always brought my knife no matter where I went, but tonight I might actually need it for something. The howling wolves weren't far ahead.

The woods were lit up by the full moon. I could see the grey shadows from the trees, and the ground was covered in dark moss that used to be green in daylight. I noticed something shiny at my feet, and I bent down to pick it up. It was the most precious jewel I'd ever seen. It didn't look like it belonged to this part of the world. There was something magical about it. I instantly felt attached to it, like it belonged to me. Its silver surface felt warm against my cold hands. Though I felt a connection with the amulet, I knew it didn't belong to me. If I took it, it would be considered stealing, and stealing was a sin. I should have left it behind, but I couldn't. I was spellbound. I kept telling myself that tomorrow I'd ask around my village to see if anyone had lost it, but I knew I'd most likely end up keeping it myself. I no longer felt afraid as I walked through the woods. The warm amulet in my hand would shield me from danger, I kept telling myself. Maybe it was a gift from God to keep my brother and me safe tonight. The howling wolves were still all over the woods, but they never got near me. It was as if the amulet warned them to keep their distance. I was almost out of the woods when I noticed a circle of light ahead of me. I quickly hid behind a tree and felt something burning in my hand. It was almost like the amulet was on fire. I should have thrown it away, but I couldn't let go of it. Instead, I put it in my pocket so it wouldn't burn my skin. That was when *their* voices broke the silence. "I was sure I brought it with me. I can even feel its presence, but I don't have it," a female voice complained.

"Fool! You should be more careful," another female voice hissed.

"Let's get out of here. We can't do anything about it now," a third woman said impatiently.

"Wait… I know the amulet is here. I can sense it. We are being watched," the first woman whispered.

Joseph Mukami Mwita
NOT DOOMED

I hope you will hear the hoot
And act accordingly
As I face you reassuringly
Without hitting you with a damn boot

It's important that you be cool
Living in the society approvingly
Cooperating around voluntarily
In that way you get something to cook

Why cover your head with a hood
It won't make you listen attentively
But if you pay attention wholeheartedly
You won't be gloomy

Be steadfast as a troop
Combating challenges squarely
And that could be a boon

It's not always easy to get a boom
But you can strike oil surprisingly
Or discover oil miraculously
In the future or soon

You will never walk with head stooped
Nor loiter carelessly
Walking will be majestically
For all your possessions aren't looted

I have let nuggets loose
To you generously
Imparting into you emphatically
So you won't be somebody's stooge

You therefore aren't doomed
For my eyes are kept on you lovingly
Without deviating inadvertently
Like I am gazing at the moon

Dr. Maria Nazos
ON THE BEACH IN ROSARITO, TIJUANA

A dog staggered over on the dark beach. It's fur half-mange,
its panting stubborn and hopeless

as love itself. That didn't stop the mutt from loving you,
nuzzling your palm, putting its head

beneath your hand. Its eyes were wild grapefruit. It smelled
of sweet rot. You backed off slowly, then fast,

past the lighthouse. As you approached the waves' edge,
there it was: the dog, floating sideways,

lifeless, in the dark surf. It had always been dying, it seemed, long
before you arrived. It was waiting to die and dead.

You waded to the body, chanting, to send up the last of its tiny
light. Then you heard

the voice, soft as dawn, the voice that knew before you did,
the whisper that you hear some nights, telling you

to let go. The voice said, *This is what happens.*
Leaving you to leave
the body, knowing where it was going, already
gone.

Previously published at voice lux journal

Marc Olmsted
CORSO DREAM

Dream: I kid with Gregory Corso poet that an android will be made identical to him like Lincoln at Disneyland. He doesn't dig this and mentions when he first saw my poetry, he said "Be careful of this one, he wants to be on top." Corso knows he got me and smiles. He then softens , starts giving poetry advice. "Write about what you know, not the President." He also mentions "Don't write about the plight of blacks, it's offensive to them."

1/7/16 morn

Image of Satellite Bar, Houston, Texas
by Brian Kenhinde

Antonia Petrone
INNER WORLD

There are places so near
yet so far from our reach.

There are moments so close
yet so distant to our eyes.

There are experiences so deep
yet so alien to our universe.

There is a world were
Places
Moments
Experiences
meet whatever distance there may be;
within the heart,
a world of its own.

Teri Petz
YOUNG AT HEART

Young at heart…other parts in desperate need of repair.
Your blood pressure medicine gives you insomnia
and the insomnia meds gave you ulcers ions ago.
Your bed is now like an Olympic ski slope
but your indigestion is still irritating your throat.
You used to party all night three four times a week
and still be functional with three hours of sleep.
Now pain gets you up and down like a yoyo all night
and you feel like a zombie day after day
from the lack of a good night's sleep.
Some days the cocktail of medications is as strong
as the drugs you used to have in the sixties
but the hallucinations are not as colourful
as they used to seem on LSD.

You tried the elimination diet to determine
what foods to avoid and you had some weird discoveries
between a gummed up state and rapid elimination
with smells that could be used for mass destruction
or state of the art torture tools by the CIA.
Some days you can only leave the house
with the toilet chained to your butt,
but you are young at heart…
with some parts in desperate need of repair.

Your skin is thin beyond hope and repair,
no amount of lotion will make it tight
like it was once upon a time.
The lines on your face are as deep
as the Grand Canyon
and you covered your grey hair for years.

You spend hours trying to find the receipt
you need to email for reimbursement
and you are convinced that the same people
that keep taking single socks from the dryer
have taken your receipt
and one day you open the scanner and there it is!

They must have returned it when you were asleep.

You mix up the names of your children,
grandchildren, the dogs, the cats and birds
you had when you were a child.
The languages you once spoke fluently
are blended into your own secret language
no one else in the world can understand.

And despite all this you keep going,
you keep smiling and you learned to laugh
in times you really wanted to cry.
Your sense of humour kept you sane
in an insane and cruel world
because you are young at heart
with some parts in desperate need of repair.

Claudia Piccinno
DAVID IS YOUR NAME
(Poem dedicated to a child with autism)

Where did your gaze stop David?
You fell on a detail in order not to see the whole.
It is not easy to decipher the compass of the senses
in the chaos of social stimuli.
And how will I support the reward
of that troublesome biology ?
To observe the failure in the connection
among your sensory abilities
it is an enormous effort for us, the"so-called normal ones".
To compensate with gestures to a shared attention,
to take you to clarify a request,
these are compelling purposes in my head.
David is your name,
you're not for me a diagnoses
or a variant or a flaw of genetic architecture,
a disregarded expectation,
an early or late intervention,
an impaired brain plasticity,
a spectrum disorder.
David is your name
the child who loves the detail. . .
I'll wear your look,
I 'll listen to your confused stereotypy
I'll go down to cross the object that attracts you
so as to shorten the distance
that keeps you confined in a room.

Paul Richmond
FAMILY TRADITIONS

I saw grandma
Run over the Tax man
With the tractor
Everyone cheered
She still went to prison
I grew up with an attitude

Everyone remembers
It as a miracle
The day I fell into the hay baler

After all the crunching sounds
Highlighted with my loud screams
I popped out the other end
In one piece
What I remember
Was being amazed
That my phone didn't get crushed
And that someone had pushed me

When I was older
I was trying to
Make my living
As a Cowboy

I started to realize
Thing weren't going as I had planned
The morning
I had to eat my horse

On my death bed
The priest who had been called
Said he wouldn't give me my last rights
I hadn't given his church any money
I asked him to lean in close
So I could shoot him at close range
With my last words
Here I come grandma

Art Paul Scholosser
ODE TO MY FRIENDS

The friends I have
Make me smile
They cheer me up
In a kindness style
Their compliments
Give me enjoyment

The friends who care
Give me hope
Takeaway despair
Like bubbles from soap
Their warm smiles
Make me go the next mile

All the memories
And the Happy days
Never seem to go away
Life with friends is better than a parade

Cartoons pages 128-129 by Art Paul Schlosser

Sankha Sen
THE LAST HARMONY

Yes, I did not fall into the Black hole, suddenly a cold breeze blew past my chin and I opened my eyes to see the golden rays of the sun touch past my eyebrows. Oh yes, it was yet another dream, but it was a Sunday. I just needed a coffee to come out of the dizzy black hole dream to land in Lucerne.

Its August and I was in my beautiful Swiss Holiday in Lucerne. Missed the Beethoven collection which I had left in Frankfurt. But the day's plan was to take a stroll across a nearby small Swiss Village called Lungern. Lara was here with me as well.

Yes, she is my girl friend about to complete her MBA. She loves Western Classical Music very much.

We planned to have our lunch at 12:00 in a Thai Restaurant. We left our car as it was in the garage in Germany for some repair so we would take the public transportation. Was thrilled for the afternoon plan.

Out of all the famous compositions, I love one composition from a person from Lake Constance (Bodensee) region of Germany. I tried to find his whereabouts but found out through local connections that he has left us few years back leaving behind his last composition. As much as I listen to his composition, it appears that something is missing in his composition, the second harmony of his composition is somewhat missing. I came to know that the intention of his composition was to find someone. This appears very interesting to me.

In the meantime, Lara complained "Oh, you are listening to the same music, haven't got ready yet?"

"Just give me a minute, I am almost done.," I somehow managed to excuse myself for being late.

Lara went to the kitchen and started making a coffee for herself.

"You are again in the blue stripes? Didn't you have anything in green?" complained Lara.

Again, I had to change to something more vegetative. Loved her smile. She grasped my hand and pulled me along. This is exactly what she does when she is happy and I am her obedient boyfriend.

It was sunny outside, people were happily roaming around, music was in the air.

It was about noon when we reached our favorite Thai restaurant. The waiters knew us and knew our favorite Menu too, as we had been eating here almost everyday.

Warm rice with Green Thai Chicken and Red Thai Duck were served. Lara hugged me once again and we said "Itadakimasu" (In Japanese, it means Let's eat) and started eating.

"It's lovely,"said Lara.

"It's perfect," I added.

The clock touched one.

We took the subways and reached the Central Station and bought a ticket for Lungern, a small Swiss village, famous for its natural beauty and lovely view of the Alps.

In the Train, I had the Love of my Life, the Music in the iPod. It's the music which looks for its missing harmony and the beauty of Switzerland all around. I am at the top of the world!

It was then 2:30 pm and we reached Lungern, which encompasses Lake Lungern beside the village of Lungern. Our plan was to take a stroll along the Lake and the church (Pfarrkirche), eventually hang around the Lungern village and return to Lucerne by evening.

There were couple of people gathered in the front of the church and someone is about to sing. We managed to slip inside the crowd and came to the front row. From there we could see the the beauty of the church; I closed my eyes and prayed to God.

"Let my love last for ever just like…." I was searching in mind whose example do I show.

And came a beautiful voice into my ears. It was a song with a harmony which sounded very similar. I have listened this song somewhere. I looked at Lara.

Lara was still listening with closed eyes. But I wanted to go closer to the singer to see who was singing. It was a beautiful middle-aged lady. I was keen to meet her and ask about the whereabouts of the song.

As the song came to an end, Lara said in a low voice, "Shall we leave now?"

I said "No, I would like to meet the singer."

She became red and said "Why?"

I said "I can't explain everything here. Let's go a little far so that we can talk loudly."

She agreed. We somehow slipped out of the crowd.

"Now what?" said Lara angrily.

I explained her the reason. She was also a music lover and so she reluctantly agreed. We went back and found that the lady is gone.

We did not go to our earlier place and just waited where we were. As everyone was trying to leave, I moved against the thin crowd pulling Lara by her hand. I reached to the organizer and asked where that Lady was who sang the song and I hummed up the song. He said that she was out there on the right. As we were about to rush to her, she appeared. We almost bumped into each other.

I said "Hallo, I am Hans and this is Lara, my girlfriend we came from Germany, but we are in our Switzerland Holidays now and staying in Lucerne. Your song appears very similar to another song. Where did you get this song? Did you compose this song yourself?"

"Aren't we going too fast? Let me introduce myself. I am Mirinda, I grew up there in that village with my mother. And to answer to your question, yes, it's her song," answered Mirinda.

"She said, she had composed this song with a purpose," explained Mirinda.

132

"What purpose," I insisted on knowing.

Mirinda with a sigh said "I wish I knew, but she left a letter with me and said if someone comes and asks about this song show him this letter.

Good that you came. You should come to my house where she lived and took her last breath."

I watched at Lara and said gloomily, "Oh God, she left us. We had other plans for today, but we would cancel those and would like to read the letter."

Lara was a bit disappointed but did understand the emotional part of the musical mystery.

Mirinda invited us in her car and drove across the beautiful Lake of Lungern. Both sides, Alps were humming in a strange harmony and it only added on the note of my ear drums.

We saw the Swiss cows grazing on the meadows and the bells ringing. Lara was quite excited and the drive took us about 15 minutes and we reached Mirinda's ancestral house on the foothills of Alps.

"The location is lovely!" said Lara loudly.

I was happy that she was enjoying this unplanned trip.

"This way," Mirinda showed us the entrance.

A middle-aged man came out and said "Hello, I am Robert, I am Mirinda's husband."

We were brought to a beautiful Living room with a grand fireplace. It was Summer but the coolness of the room provided us some relief. "Would you like to have some coffee?" said Robert.

We said, "It's okay no need to stress yourself."

Robert said "The coffee machine would take the stress, it's okay. "

Mirinda came back after parking her car in the garage and changing herself a bit and requested Robert "Honey one Expresso also for me!". Robert said, "I am already at it, honey!".

There were two portraits of two teenagers, a boy, and a girl. Mirinda nodded "That's Michael and that's Beatrice, my two beautiful kids. They are with their Aunty spending their Summer holiday in French Riviera".

We were satisfied and felt what a lovely happy family it was.

Robert brought coffee for all of us and some beautiful hand made cup cakes and cookies, probably baked by Mirinda. And some typical Swiss chocolates.

Lara just jumped to start with the chocolates. I just indicated that she shouldn't behave childish here.

We too lightly spoke of our plans and brought the same topic of the song. Mirinda stopped us and said, "I wanted to show you something upstairs" We knew what it could be. She took us to a room with lot of beautiful artistic portraits.

Mirinda continued "This is the room of my mother, Paula, she actually composed the song and left a letter with me. She taught me singing throughout her life."

"What letter", I said.

Then she opened her Almirah and pulled a drawer and brought a letter out and handed over to us. The letter was somewhat old and the writings were also somewhat damaged. But I could read it.

The letter comprised: -

"The last harmony could it be
Lost love will it always ignite ….
Long gone may be me
Do find him for us to unite ….

With love
Paula"

134

Mirinda said "She expired in Reading in England."
We found this letter in her hand as she took her last breath.

I asked her "What about your father?"

Mirinda said "My father was a Marine Engineer and travelled almost 10 months elsewhere. Initially mom used to travel with him but later when I started going to school, she couldn't and later my father expired in a shipwreck near Hawaii Island. She spent almost her last 40 years with me and her music. My mother and I, we stayed in Reading at my father's house, where she left her last breath."

She said she had learned music from her childhood.

I said "This song which you sang is very similar to the one which I hear always. Strangely it was just a mere recording from radio show. Don't know who sang the song. I would play the song now and please sing your portion and we would hear how the harmonies really match."

I played the song with Bluetooth speakers and Mirinda started singing her version.

As she started singing, the cuckoo started blowing. A gash of wind blue across the room, the bells in the room started shimmering. This is the moment!

Robert entered the room and said, "Something is happening!"

"It's lovely" said Lara.

"It is the *Last Harmony*", I continued, "This means Paula wanted to unite with the soul who composed this song. We need to find him."

"But how" said Mirinda.

"Leave that to me, I know who forwarded this song recording.", I assured Mirinda.

Mirinda just broke down and sat in the sofa, she was full of tears and informed us "Paula grew up in St. Gilgen and learnt all her music there."

St. Gilgen is about less than about 30 km from Salzburg. This beautiful scenic little town was used as the backdrop for several scenes for the movie, 'The Sound of Music.' St. Gilgen is also many times called as Mozart village because the composer's mom was born in this little town. Moreover, Mozart's sister stayed here and his grandfather also worked there.

Robert intercepted "Oh you both must have planned a trip here. Don't worry we would drive you to some beautiful places here in Lungern."

Robert said "This natural paradise, surrounded by mountain trails, is the perfect destination for nature lovers and hikers alike. Almost every valley you pass through in Switzerland seems to have a stunningly beautiful lake. Lungern is just like one of them as you'll see the Lungernsee, or Lake Lungern. The climate is really pleasant here."

It was almost 4 pm then. We stopped at a spot near Lungern Lake. Lara was busy taking some beautiful photos for her Instagram.

Robert said, "Why don't you have dinner with us and take the first train tomorrow may be?"

I said, "Thanks for the offer but maybe next time."

"Okay I will drive you to the station," Robert said.

Lara said, "Thanks a lot, it was lovely meeting you all here. Never expected that Lungern would mean so much to us. Please do visit us in Germany."

We hugged each other and reluctantly departed Lungern.

After returning to Lucerne we stayed for one more night and returned to Germany.

A week had passed; I scrolled all my messages to find out who had sent me this recording. It came from a friend who stays near Lake Constance in South Germany. I called him but unfortunately the number doesn't exist. But I had his email ID and contacted him.

I called Lara. "This weekend we need to travel to Lake Constance to meet a friend, named Markus."

The bell rang, I knew it was Lara. She told from the entrance "Come down I am in the car."

I was almost ready and locked my doors. It was a Mercedes C Class.

She said, "I hired it at the station."

As we took the Autobahn (German Highways), I played the song. Lara's eyes were wet.

"I hope we find who the singer was," said Lara.

Around noon we reached Lake Constance. Lake Constance, at the foothills of the Alps, joins three countries—Germany, Austria and Switzerland. This beautiful stretch of water is a most awaited holiday destination throughout the year. The lake bears the shores of picturesque towns; from here we could also see the beautiful mountain range of the Alps.

Markus invited us for a small cruise ride from Lindau.

There is a direct ferry departing from Lindau Hafen to Meersburg.

Lara parked the car at a suitable place and we went to the ferry and met Markus.

Markus was a tall man; he is an Austrian who moved to Germany for his studies.

"Hallo Hans, how are you? It's been long, we met," Markus said.

We hugged each other, then I introduced Lara, they greeted each other and we proceeded towards the ferry.

Lara had never been to Lake Constance. "What a lovely place, thanks for the ride," said Lara.

We went to the outside, went on to the railings. We ordered something to drink.

"Yes, so hope you are doing great?" I said.

"Yes, life has been fair to me. Shall I throw some light on the recorded music?" said Markus.

"Yes, off course," said I.

Lara nodded too.

Markus said, "The song was composed by my grandfather. He grew up in St.Gilgen. He said this to me before he expired."

Markus please play my last song called 'Last Harmony' in the Radios and if someone comes to meet you, please give her this letter.

I did it as my father had some source in local Radio broadcasting office. Then I sang this in the radios and I recorded the song after it was broadcasted and sent across in WhatsApp to friends only hoping if someone comes."

Markus had brought the letter along and took it out from his pocket.

"Oh, it was you who sang the song, you sang beautifully. Give me the letter," I said.

The letter comprised: -

"My soul will be in the Blues of Constance
My song will allure the air of Trance
Last harmony is mere game of chance
Oh dear, will you ever unite to my romance?"

"He studied English as a second language," said Markus.

"What was his name?" I asked.

"His name was Paul," Markus answered.

"What a coincidence? She was called Paula. They were meant to be together. They grew up in the same village, probably learned same kind of music and departed by destiny. They couldn't meet each other since then but their romance was always alive and this song was composed although differently but what a musical coincidence, they are in perfect match when we play the two songs together. One harmony compliments the other," I concluded.

I called Mirinda directly and explained the whole situation. She was heartbroken and full of tears. She said that she wanted to come there the next day and see the letter.

Markus too welcomed them and was also keen to meet them.

Markus said "He was buried near to Lake Constance as he lived his last years here. Please do stay with us here for the night and tomorrow we can meet Mirinda."

We agreed.

Mirinda and Robert reached around 13:00.

"Welcome here, hope you had a nice drive?" I greeted them in.

Markus had served lunch for all of us. We were offered lovely trout from the Lake. With Lemon and Breads and home-made salads, the lunch was very nice.

From Robert's apartment we get a nice view of the Lake.

Markus learned singing as well, I knew that and Mirinda too regularly sings in choirs.

I took up the chance and requested Mirinda and Markus both, to sing the song together and complete the union of the Souls.

We went on the Balcony and watched the Lake and Mirinda and Markus started singing.

A gentle Wind blew across our face, the trees were moving. It appeared as if the Heaven were eagerly waiting to hear this *Last Harmony* and listen to the union of the two longing souls. Lara was full of emotion and was recording this moment in her mobile.

I closed my eyes and saw Paul and Paula sailing on a boat and singing the *Last harmony* and were happy and nothing could stop them of the ecstasy of their hearts uniting in the melody of their harmony.

An unfinished song found its meaning in the blues of Lake Constance.

As the song was finished. Robert said, "You two should record the song in a Studio."

"Great idea," I said.

Markus said, "Okay I will search a studio and would see when we could record this."

We found one Studio and found a date luckily the next day.

Markus had a big and spacious apartment and Mirinda didn't want to lose the chance to give justice to the love of her mother's life.

In the late afternoon we visited the graveyard to pay our homage to the soul of Paul.

Mirinda and Markus both read the respective letters and sang once again the song *Last Harmony*.

Next day due to the digitalization of music industry, the person at the Studio nicely filled the song with his musical arrangements and we received our master copy of the song *Last Harmony*. The Studio said they would make good amount of copies and would send this song to the Radio broadcasting office.

One month later, on a Sunday evening the song was broadcasted in Germany as well as in Switzerland.

And off course I can imagine that Paul and Paula were holding their hands in the heaven and were listening to their unfinished song and were in tears.

All of us were heavy in our hearts and we decided to frame the two letters and keep it with us.

The song *Last Harmony* was liked by many people and they came to know about the Love story of Paul and Paula.

I kept watching their letters and called Lara. "Hey I feel we need to go to the Lake Constance once again."

Lara said, "What a coincidence, I too felt the same thing."

On a lonely weekend, Lara and I, decided to visit Lake Constance once again. We went up to the shores of the Lake and read out a poem written by me: -

"Departed are the notes, not the minds
For whom the music is just a melody
It's the longing which matters, for those who craves for the harmony
The smell over the Lake, the blue of the depth
The Mountains of hearts echoes in the Harmony of love
Paul and Paula are not just two names
Who signed off their hope to smile a tender breath?
Somewhere deep in their lives burned a pain of despair
Not knowing about the Union in their lives,
Confident minds left a token of hope
Fulfilling their desire, bestowing in the eternity....

They came and they went, left a touch of noteless Romance
The notes of the Last Harmony let vibrate with Nature's resonance."

This story is originally published in the book "Collection of Feeling" published by Haoajan in Kolkata, India. Reviewed and modified a bit by the author afterwards.

Pankhuri Sinha
COMING BACK TO THE ALLIANCE STATEMENT

Coming back to the alliance statement
After such robbery of rights
In broad day light
The robbery of credit, merit, opportunity
The great big thrill
Of doing it yourself
The thrill that in the modern day
Has been solely accepted as the individual's
Stolen, brutally
In the making of an unnecessary alliance
Consisting of marriage, social forces
Nationality, all kinds of identities
Even the question of an ongoing affair
An extra marital affair
Made into the central issue
And put forth at the centre
Preventing work
Preventing progress
But primarily
An alliance
Made up of a proximity
Between work and family
Most undesirable
Never permitted
An alliance
That has still eluded
Still outpaced you
Still resisted being busted
Like a drug trafficking racket
Wearing the mask of righteousness

Eliott Slinn
EVERYTHING COMES TO PASS

I've heard it said
Everything comes to pass
Some things are built to break
While others are built to last
You touched my skin so softly
Like fog upon the grass
It was then that I knew
Everything comes to pass
Your eyes were bright as diamonds
Your smile sharp as glass
I found your little letter
It said your love was on a fast
So I tied you to my poem
And packed you in my past
The priest said on Sunday
That everything comes to pass

RezaUddin Stalin
THE BEGINNING

My time is split like a cow's hoof
the moments are chapped like the dark feet of the farmer
My birth does not refer to a time
and the events are not chained by the moment.

When nothing is happening in the world
is time than static like a question mark
Do I want to recognize time only from fear of death?

To a paleontologist a thousand years is nothing
to a philosopher, a century is a triviality
to an astronomer, a hundred million years is an instant.

But my time has affected me like a thirst
I have recognized the moments before the event
and determined the start before a journey.

For an unborn embryo, no time is begun in the world
Without the cry of birth
driven by a prior event
is the embryo bereft of event?

My time is split like a cow's hoof
the moments are chapped like the dark feet of the farmer
Before my birth, there was no auspicious time in the world
My cry heralded the beginning of the world.

Joanna Svensson
WHEN THE RAIN STOPPED CRYING

I sense the fragrance of your shadow
The fragrance that
You brought along
To the other side of the rain

I can still feel
The unspoken words
Hanging in the air
Hoovering like raindew

Words unsaid
Words unspoken
That I have longed so long to hear

Empty spaces
Yet filled with yearning
Filled with yearning
And tears of rain

The rain has cried for me
The wind has swept me
In the lukewarm breeze
Of a summer's afternoon

A breeze that still remembers
So well that last late evening
When the unspoken words
At least got the color
Of the shy wild roses
Of pale fragrance of pink

And so I waited
Waited for the day
A day I thought
That never would come
But still did come at last

At a place so precise
At exactly the same time
Right like bang on the dot
Just the moment
When you will be
On the other side of the rain

And now I am here
Right where I had forseen
The unspoken words were told
To me by someone else

Someone who could sense them
Someone who could rephraise them
And bless them all
And fill with flair
And give them life and beauty

Oh, I know that you see
Through the rain all this
And I know that you regret
That you did the deeds you did

The unspoken words
That now have been spoken
Have all got new meaning
And the crying rain
Has all stopped!

Annette Tarpley
FROM SUNSET TO SUNRISE

She sat on a hill, observing the sunset
The sun slowly disappearing on the horizon
With it's daily display of breathtaking art
Colors playfully dancing, meshing, repositioning

The sunset mimicking her own life
The finality of a day now passed
Once here, real and vibrant
Now a memory of a day gone…with a history

What played out, in a day that was given
Each person, well aware of the cast
Who would be a part of the performance
In their own worldly reality

At last, losing its battle for the spotlight
The sun relinquished control to the moon
Changing its cyclic appearance
The moon makes its silent solo

Surrounded by its twilight companions
Twinkling in their heavenly realm
The woman now privy to this nocturnal serenade
As she lay on the grass gazing at the celestial display

The moon in its fullness of glory
Shining light, yet shadows were cast
What would lie in store for her
When nightfall relinquished its lunar pull

The sunrise awoke her
Content she was in knowing
The dawn of the day shed light
Onto the uncertainty of today

Paru Timilsina
COCKROACH THAT LIVES WITH ME

A lone bird unicorn
Lives with me
Since she was born
She is magical
Also, real trouble creator
She sees life
through my eyes
Listens my sound
to synchronize
And
whispers
'I am judging you'

She loves my shadow
And call herself wise
Any moment
I smile
She licks my breath
And taste my life

She eats butter like dessert
Yoghurt like cheese
Sometime
 I guess
She doesn't have taste
Cause,
She eats my words
When I bake cakes

We live together
Like a peer
May be,
 Fairy tales are myth
But my unicorn is real
She knows my truth
And guess my lies
Prove my words
With her believing eyes

Her roar is louder
then storm
Her silence is stronger
Like death
Every time I call
Her unicorn
She holds her smile
With faith

I can see your illusion
And disbelief
What objection can you have?
Everything you touched
Will vanish in a flash
I can clearly imagine
How you feel
Listening story of your life
I steal

Look,
I stopped for you
Even I know
I can't break
Your hardcore
For sure
How can I be secure?
When You poison
my unicorn
before repairing
your private doors
I see,
Everyone eyes fall upon her
As if she is little monster
Fools even ask questions
Why she's not white?
 Where's her next tentacle?

You baffle me
How long will you
Make her your
Centre of attention?

better have courage
to respect our kingdom
Oh! My dear morons
Here again
You heard me wrong
She is my unicorn.

Igor Ursenco
THE DAILY NEOPHYTE'S CHALLENGES

Don't you ever trust The 3 "W"-es
in the United Kingdom – namely Weather, Work and Women – warns me
my ad hoc tube neighbour sat next to me. "Well,

and Wankers too", adds he
wandering if Londoner weekends are safe
anymore for own Witty Celebration. If this guy
won't get off by Paddington station, I definitely will
loose the trust in Oscar Wilde's sense
of personal ridiculousness. The same

happened to me as I entered as early as yesterday
my local `Marks & Spencer` store, being aware
that I might get out back eventually wrapped in all new
clothes rather that in my old fashioned & warm
philosophy.

Amrita Valan
POETRY AS I SEE IT

Poetry to me is the voice of angels. It speaks when you let go the control of left-brain logos and allow yourself to dissociate from urgency and purpose.

As I was reflecting on it the other day, in a comment on a poem to a friend, where she said there was a method to its madness, it struck me, not only is there a method to the madness, but the madness is in fact necessary, an inherent part of true poetry.

You can have tons of craft and skill, and while they enhance a poem, a true poem is born of genuine feeling, a torrential tsunami, distilled and compressed into a rhapsody if you will.

So, the best poems, are a fount of emotions, where the flow is directed with precision, using the literary devices, of rhyme and meter, enjambments, alliterations, metaphors, similes, maintaining an overall unity and integrity of tone and mood.

Yet poems devoid of craft, bare and naked in its emotional vulnerability and truth, can shine like a gem, even with a few linguistic flaws.

I am a grammar Nazi, I detest anything that takes away from a poem, avoidable mistakes in gender, tense, number and so on...But if a word isn't the best objective fit, yet it enhances the poem's theme, if it works, I call it serendipity, the Muse at work.

To me a poet needs a solid understanding of the language of expression, which a high school student who loves literature may have. You do not need an advanced degree in literature.

A doctoral degree may enable you to perfectly craft a rondeau, a cleave, a sestina or a villanelle, yet a lack of the flow of vital emotions, the courage and honesty to share your vulnerability, makes the artiest best crafted poem somehow ineffective and lifeless.

Craft and skill gets trumped by emotional richness and imaginative grandeur. Every time. In a poem, it is the heart which is in the driver's seat of the vehicle, and it will out miraculously rabbits from the bottomless hat of creativity, if you trust it and silently listen.

The brain or mind can then be the assistant the skilful secretary that proofreads the poem, but the valiant and vulnerable human heart is its real author.

Amrita Valan
THE PROPOSAL

He sat me down on a plush sofa couch
In an elegant nook,
A stately French window did it overlook
And from the corner of wide-open eyes
I espied, a comely, crystal gurgling brook.

And marvelled at the natural wealth
Of his lavish family estate vast
And waited with inner trepidation
As his mother made her visitation.

And asked me how soon I could decide
To become her first born's suitable bride
I caressed the long stemmed rose he gave

Kim Vodicka
SOFTER ENDING

When you come,
I hope you come flowers.

　　　I hope you come me
　　　several seven dozens
　　　and brown-paper-bag them.

　　　　　Mass-marketed seminal flora.

　　　　　Taste and see the beauty of
　　　　　Our Lady of
　　　　　Two-Dimensional
　　　　　Hearts.

　　　Floratozoa and fructescence
　　　manure'd twice daily,
　　　in partial sun, partial shade.

Our Lady of
Photosynthegenic.

　　　　　　Dr. Kellogg would not approve.

　　　　　　He thought each time you came flowers,
　　　　　　you lost a bit of brain power.

　　　　　　He recommended a steady diet
　　　　　　of dull and drab
　　　　　　to subdue the urge
　　　　　　to come flowers.

　　　　　　That's how cornflakes were born.

　　　　　　Taste and see the beauty of
　　　　　　Our Lady of
　　　　　　the Cornflake
　　　　　　Come Flowers.

155

Sprinkled on our crap crop
in equal parts mockery
and dishonor.

How she made erections everywhere
explode ever more violently
and reinvented flower power.

It was an accident,
so I gather
like the flowers
in our garden.

Rising,
though earth burdened.

Rising
from two-dimensional heart
shit.

When the time came
to exhume our yield,
the time went.

On the morning after
the debauch-off.

Our very first leaf-and-petal
happening event.

There's no way
we could've artfully dodged
this.

The exhuming of our first rose
from the best hole,
mummified
for forever-keeping.

Photo of Kim Vodicka at Brickhouse, Jonesboro AR

Photo by Mary Kyle

Dr. Duane Vorhees
AN ANGLER'S TALE

Born by the river
I became quite familiar
with the local fishing holes.
With my treasured fishing pole
I caught my share of trophy
bluegills, sunfish, and crappies.
Though truth to tell, I must say
some of the best got away,
my hook was always baited.

Lazy and satiated,
I was the last to expect
that I'd be the one netted
by some patient hungry girl
borne by the river.

Raymond Walker
THE BRANGUEIL.
THE SOURCE

Imagine a bright light shining from behind you focused on what lies before your eyes, draping it in your own shadow. This light shining into the mouth of a deep cavernous hollow filled with dripping stalactites, its floor covered in stunted weeping stalagmites and the bones of dead things. The sun behind your head just before Helios draws it back into ocean allowing his sister Selene to take to the heavens leaving you once more staring into the darkness. To see this shattered woman.

Remember the long walk to this place of shadows and undiscovered dreams. Yellow blooms dot the many gorse bushes that infringe upon the narrow deer trail, that winds between pine and rowan, oak and sycamore trees. Wild mint and garlic scent the air along with the all pervasive pine sap. These trees shaded my life, these trees have always been here, sometimes of one shape and scent another time; another tree but this forest has always been here. It first formed as the ice withdrew from Eurasia as the lands parted and the continents that we know today formed. This forest existed when Britain was not an island, before Scotland was a country, before the highland divide was created, before the volcanoes and earthquakes that moved the crust of this world, ripped my country, apart.

It is a quiet day. No howling monstrosities borne on and in the wind that echo so often here that I have grown acclimated to the wail of the banshee and the sudden summer storm. No swirling ghosts where the arctic and southern winds combine and swirl, lifting trash from the pavements and whipping the dust and detritus into every bare face as Is the norm here. Instead it is still; only a breath of salt wind heading in sluggishly from the North Atlantic to lull those that live here into the false sense of security that they may yet live another year so close to me.

Eventually I eat them all.

Were I to turn I would see it behind me, green and grey and growling, vast, dark and deep in all it's majesty but I am busy grasping roots and grass, drawing myself ever upwards over a fine rock scree pebbles and boulders interspersed with the hardiest of alpine plants searching for a cave.

Imagine tonight's sunset Illuminating the eternal darkness that has existed in this cavern before humankind has discovered how to walk upright. Australopithecus, Ramapithecus, Neanderthals, Homo erectus all will have looked into this darkness. Imagine, now, it was not those living fossils but you who looked into this suddenly brightly lit, shadow strewn cave and before you in the darkness cast only by your own shadow you saw a person, a bloodied and broken person; criss-crossed by the shadows cast by your arms, torso, legs and head in the shattering illumination cast from a drooping sun, each limb, each feature skewed by the light and angle, shadow and attenuated shape.

Consider the depths of a woman's sorrow. Eve, the originator, the unblessed, the tempted one. Ruth, the kind one, maimed and subjected to the hate of all because she was not Hebrew, Edith is turned into a pillar of salt for being curious, Mary Magdalene herself abused and cursed, Clytemnestra, abandoned and unloved, Penelope, left alone whilst her husband philandered, Helen, used, again and again by men.

Such misuse, exploitation, disregard and slavery had in the mists of time been noted. But we were new and different, modern men no longer hurt women, no longer made them the slaves of Christian tradition, such as marriage, unless the slave consented, unless the woman wished to be enslaved.

She stood before my gaze, bloodied and broken.

By the god, call him what you will. By the gods, the pantheon, the singular, the plural the diverse, the reborn and the sadistic. Call him nature. Call him a daemon. Call him what you will but no matter what and when you name him you will hear too many women screaming, whimpering, squealing, weeping, squalling, whaling, simpering, washing tears from tear streaked faces that the gods, the god, the hope, the one, alpha, had to intervene.

The Barangueil had existed before even the gods and the god, she had formed when men were not men and women not women, little more than apes and still in the thrall of the stronger male. Barangeil did not know the term for her sex, when she was first summoned into being, this worlds gods were opaque, their motives, unknown even to them, unknown to her.

She was formed from the raw stuff of gods and stars and cruelty. The alpha, at that time known only as the male would soon become a god of sorts, seminally worshipped by those Ramapithecus beginning to grow aware.

And as they, the proto hominids began to think they wondered and gazed at the night sky and thought; how did we get here?

Who created us?

What formed our being?

And those thoughts unanswered drifted for many years and grew and grew until the hominids that could think and wonder thought to themselves. We were created, such as the animals we eat such as the grass we walk upon. Those hominids then asked the eternal question; Who made us?

Gods based on the beliefs of the hominids jumped into being, an explanation was needed and there was no science no understanding. We gave the egos the names of those that scared us, terrified us, preyed upon us. Snake gods, wolf gods, tiger gods, spider gods, we were terrified and we tried to appease them.

Then into the halls of the gods another appeared.

A dweller in the dark places of the mind, For women have always been downtrodden, lesser beings than men, shuffled over, shed aside for newer lovers, discarded, swept off like dandruff from an afflicted shoulder.

Remember the past, where we were, staring into the cavern, seeing the woman in the shadows. Criss-crossed by welts and burns, scars and shadows. Imagine that she welcomed you home.

1.

I was young when my mother first told me of Branguiel. Stories of the one that lives in the mist, the haunted girl, the forsaken one. The maimed girl, she who bore the scars of womankind. She never spoke or mentioned her name. My mothers silent face sat above mine, tears running from the shadowed lashes of her green eyes, her face bruised, her lip bleeding, the scarf she had wrapped around her head hid few of the contusions, the bruises, the cuts that she often bore when my father returned from any of his travels. She thought me too young to understand but I understood much even at such a young age. I lay back on my narrow bed and looked back up at her tear streaked face.

I had fallen running, playing, climbing trees and knew how each cut and scrape felt, how each bruise burned and hurt before growing purple then red with yellow on the outside then green and yellow before it faded forever leaving only tiny scars that sometimes even I could not see. Each of those tiny scars hurt and each and every one made me angry, each burned more than the one before.

Imagine now a young boy with fading bruises comforted by a mother with tears streaming from her eyes. Bloodied, bruised and cut. This remembered mother taking solace in the one good thing in her life. Her child, blood of her blood, birthed from her loins, a part of her, separate but conjoined.

And then look at the child who lies beneath her, half asleep, on the verge of crying himself due to his mothers distress. Small, his meagre body outlined beneath the thin white sheet folded down over the deep blue knitted blanket. His blue eyes cold and furious though his lip trembles and his wide but thin lipped mouth quakes with emotion, the hair on his head dark and rumpled with sleep stands straight.

Even now, so many years later I remember my mother gazing down, her green swollen eyes on mine. Was she worried that I had heard the beating? I had not that particular night but that made no difference, I had heard many more whimpering's, many more explosions of breath, cries, pleas to stop, before that night. I had heard her squeals, heard the blunt trauma, a base drum with suppression. I heard the cries and arguments, the punches landing. The breathing.

You never hear someone breathing unless you are concentrating on it. Everyone breathes but you never hear it unless someone is ill or asthmatic, it is simply something that everyone does. But you do when the air disappears suddenly from a body. And the breath shuddered from my mothers body to often.

I see, though I am prone in my bed, each move of the battle, I hear the breathing, the struggle, the breakage, and feel each of the wounds inflicted. My father suggesting that my mother had found a lover when he was away. She had not, she had rarely left my side in the time he was gone.

My Mother telling him not to be stupid, I heard the bottle top unscrewed again, the crack and clink of ice put in a glass and the glug, glug sound made by a narrow mouthed bottle, for the forth or fifth time. The bottle of bourbon would be emptying now I imagined. For my father never poured small measures such as those I saw on the television or in films. The tumbler was always full. At least when he started, it was.

I heard muttered whispers, then voices rising, a glass smashed then a chin. Dull whumps as the air left a punched stomach or side. Whimpers and searing spittle spurted curses from my father. "whore". Meek acceptance from my mother. I saw nothing but I knew, I envisioned each and every comment and punch and I knew, and the rage grew in me and the rage rooted itself deeply into my perception of the world, rooted itself into my being, my mind, perhaps even my soul.

2.

Imagine a small house, slotted together with many others of the same type and style, houses on parade, each as similar outside as they were different on the inside.

On a warm summer evening these houses would come alive with children playing in the streets, women hanging out washing, to be dried the next day, men sitting on makeshift stools made from tyres or bricks; drinking beer whilst the lazy sun set. And these were the halcyon days.

Bruised and bloody, two months early, having been pushed down the stairs by my father in a drunken rage, my mother gave birth to another child and I had a sister.

Mara.

She was, as all babies are, a squealing brat desirous of my mothers milk, warmth and comfort. Then as babies do, she grew and became a person, a small spindly girl but still a person.

And for the very first time in my life I fell in love. So small, so helpless, so breakable, I swore to myself to protect her from my father, I would kill him to save her if I had to.

I hatched plans. Laying beneath the kitchen table and slicing the tendons at the back of his ankles as he walked by with a Stanley knife. When He could not move I would cut his throat. When He was in the bath, though he rarely bathed, we were used to his stink, there was a socket just outside the toilet and I imagined unscrewing the bolt that held the door closed, A toaster in the bath would do for him.

Despite my elaborate plans and wishes I never needed to kill him.

When my father had not been drinking, when he was not tired he was fun to be around, he would play with me and my younger sister, he would be kind to us, loving and a good father. I do not think that he knew that I and my little sister would stay awake waiting for the punch, the scream, the whimper, we always knew that every so often they would come and Mara would pull back the covers from her own small bed and crying, run to my bed and I would hold her in my arms all night.

This was no hardship she was little and warm and would fall asleep quickly as I lay awake and listened to the noises of the night. I could hear owl's hooting and nightingales, even foxes rooting around outside the windows looking to scavenge our leftovers. Mostly I heard subdued screams, whimpers and weeping.

Look at me lying awake at night, staring up at the ceiling of our small council house constructed in the early years of the twentieth century to provide homes for those few who returned from the great war, my tiny and frail sister curled in beside me, each leaching warmth from the other and each taking comfort from the other.

And I imagining all the ways that I could hurt and kill my father.

I Imagined stabbing him with a knife, a farm implement but often thought that too quick, I wished him to suffer. I wished his pain to last, I wanted him to beg forgiveness for all that he had done to our mother. These thoughts were nothing other than fantasies created in my own head. I was not my father. Nothing like him, and could not bring myself to crush a spider underfoot even though I detested them, never mind punch or hurt another person.

The other boys in school considered me a wimp and I was relentlessly bullied.

Look at my mother; small, her pearl shaped face pretty in it's own odd way as it oft loomed over her two children, Mara and I, at night. A taste for sugar and sweet things had discoloured many of her teeth and those infected had grown black. I suspected that she would have been pretty otherwise.

The short golden penumbra of hair, drawn close to her scalp seemed like a halo to us; her children. Her hair drawn tight and close may have been a curse for I know; whispered voices in other rooms. My father did not like it.

Of sturdy stock, my mothers father and mother, our grandparents, rather rotund, seemingly happy were, I thought; good people.

I did not trust my perceptions in the way I once had. My mother eschewing the family proclivities had grown thin over the years with worry and angst. No more than can be expected.

The first time the police visited neither Mara nor I had noticed a thing, sleeping deeply, each in our own beds. but the neighbours across the road had head things, noticed things.

A stranger, walking past, had called the authorities as my mother fled the house and had witnessed my father punching her. Our front lawn was small, barely fourteen feet to a side and my mother had not even made it to end of the grass before he caught her and punched her. In front of a stranger, a woman walking her dog in the evening.

The embarrassment meant more than the harm done to my mother after all she was used to it, almost complicit in her own torture. Otherwise why would she put up with it?

We were used to it.

3.

Mara no longer shared my bed at night, she was growing up and though still a child had been indoctrinated by her friends at school. Then thunder and lightning broke the sky, and a small body would still worm it's way into my bed and pull the covers over her head and hold me; warm and lovely until morning came.

View Mara; A slight child, obviously akin to her brother and father but different from her mother. The strangest of things as both my father and I were there for her birth. Only later was I to think that my fathers claims of my mothers infidelity were so far fetched as to be ridiculous. We were so obviously his children even were we to have it tattooed on our foreheads the proof would not be more obvious.

Mischievous darting blue eyes, scanned the all of everything, a questioning mouth with girls lips wider and more sensual than her brothers, a small nose and beautiful blue eyes, heavy lidded as were my own but in her case framed with long dark lashes. Mara was a jewel. Bearing all the handsome wonder of my fathers younger self, that had attracted my mother, in a truly feminine and uncorrupted renewal of my father. Young enough and lucky enough to sleep through all the drama, Mara blossomed and remained blissfully unaware of the circumstances of my mother and fathers death.

For this I am Glad.

4.

Mara was lucky, too young, to remember all the things that went on, she slept through most of them as I lay awake, her small body curled against mine.

I heard it all, the curses, the punches thrown the impacts, I saw the bruises and never accepted my mothers excuses and so contrived in my bed at night, Mara curled into my side, my mother weeping in an another room, to kill my father.

I had it planned perfectly, many years of sitting at night watching TV "Silent Witness", "Morse", "Taggart", "Dexter" and Rebus had informed me of all I had to do but even that was taken from me as the bastard died of a heart attack before I had the chance to do anything.

Imagine a sad day at the funeral home. Burnished mahogany coffin paid for by my fathers insurance, white silk draped my father. The coffin seemed buffered with silk and padding as though he may be shaken around as the ground opened up and hell swallowed him.

Perhaps they meant his cadaver to enter the flames unharmed.

I looked sad at the funeral and in a way I think that I was, my father may have beaten the living daylights out of my mother but apart from the occasional slap (a common practice at the time) he never hurt me. I asked Mara about it one night after we had too much red wine and told her that I had always wondered if he was dodgy with her when I was not there but she assured me that he was nothing other than good with her as he always had been with me. I believed her.

He was a shit but only with the one person.

Imagine a brother and sister sitting at a funeral, one in a dark suit and black tie, the other in widows weeds even though she is a vital and beautiful girl. The sun, diffuse as it was works it's way through the stained glass windows in the nave, prints patterns upon her face as she kneels. Her brother immobile beside her.

He will not knell even though it is his own fathers funeral. He will say goodbye to the fellow but inwardly shout hurrah for his mothers sake. She, his mother is weeping up a storm and he feels this silly, she should be glad to have him gone, to see the end of him, to know that she never needs to beg again, never needs to be hit again.

He is too young to know but he will learn loneliness as we all do over time.

It is not your friend.

5.

Imagine a time a few years later, the perceptions of the population and seasons have changed and passed in the flicker of an eye. Imagine a sad depressed fellow staring at a computer screen and then calling his sister.

An ex-girlfriend had told the press that he had taken advantage of her. He was not accused of rape but rather exploitation.

I explained to Mara, "The girl in the story cared much more for me than I had for her and so I had taken advantage of her by loving her for only a short time". I was accused of the same shortly after, the first girlfriend left, upset and annoyed with me, the second outraged that I should leave her and so I imagined myself the soul of my father. I told Mara of my worry one night and she assured me that it was not true but I could see her look in my eye assessing me, wondering if I was just an offshoot from the same branch.

I wondered the same myself.

I had never hit a woman, never will.

But I could not kid myself, I had been unkind to a few over the years. I had not always loved those that loved me, I had not always been completely fair nor honest.

Was I perhaps my father in a different age? One where you would neither slap nor punch a woman, but would still treat them in the same way mentally?

6.

This preyed upon my mind constantly and that started my search. I could not believe that I was my father returned to this earth. Never had I hurt a woman physically but I was aware that I had mentally. Much as some women had hurt me. Love is not always returned as it is given.
Though I wish the world of love and sex easier than it has been.

The Branguiel. (My mother had once told me of her, the epitome of the woman scorned) Had been a courtier of Cyrus, the king of kings, heir at the time to the Persian throne and had endured his ministrations. Women to him were playthings and he enjoyed torturing them especially during sex, He would brand his charm upon them as he came within them. He could then remember which of his harem he had impregnated. Branguiel was barren or had some way to avoid impregnation of the monsters children and so he branded her over and over until his death in 530BC

7.

Imagine the days you have taken walking over the heather encrusted hills to get here to the far north west of Scotland. How tired you were, how exhausted, too many hills, too many glens, too many forests you have had to make your way through, too many rivers to ford and so you arrive at your goal exhausted and broken as the creature you face.

The years of research, pouring over books, sitting in front of screens, too little movement, too much food, too passionate about your subject, too focused, letting real life go by without a thought or even noticing your life disappearing as you focus on your task, your obsession.

Imagine a bright October day, an occluded sun shining brightly over a frost covered endless sea of green and brown hills, separated only by hedges and streams. You have left the car behind, many miles away now as you drag your, corpulent exhausted body over another hill, through another river.. And Another. Undertaken this longest of treks.

The Branguiel, the woman who was wronged. Stands within the mouth of the cave and gazes at me.

My father wronged my mother.

I wronged many in my romantic encounters.

I come to ask forgiveness. of womankind I say into the dark mouth of the cave and unto the presence waiting there.

She is scarred, whipped, I see the fronds on every piece of available skin, the marks, the scars.

I stand and ask her; she who is the weeper. The Branguiel, she who weeps for the women. Am I the same? Am I the monster my father was?

The tears run from her face, they weep over the scars and tattoo's of her abuses, that cover every part of her face and seen skin. Am I the enemy?

I see the small motions on her face the tics at the corners of her mouth, the flinch in her eyes as she tries to draw herself from my gaze but I saw also, myself, young and full of my own power, a power I used mercilessly when I could. To seduce, subdue women to my will.

Young, quiet, no sportsman nor the brightest in the room, I sat observing, considering or reading.

Just the same as I did standing in the cave mouth. The sun shone behind me as I stood shadowing it from her.

This broken woman, this shade born from times past. And I asked Am I guilty?

8.

Yes.
She said.
All men are, you no more than most.

Yet like many women I have also been hurt in love
and so I asked before she faded back into the shadows

"Am I a bad person?

Before I even asked the question with a shake of her skeletal fingers she admonished me;

You seek forgiveness. All of those girls and there are many, too many for you to imagine, they seek a peace that they shall never have.

How dare you ask for forgiveness?

I heard a whisper as she moved back into the cave…..no one is true in love.

9.

It was a long walk back to the car. A long drive from the far west coast back to the city and even longer negotiating the traffic through Glasgow to Mara's house.
Ewan was at work, a nurse at the southern general hospital. Late shift.
We had time to speak as we rarely had since dad died.
Imagine a brother and sister, siblings, each so different from the other that all they have in common is their childhood. Each reminiscing about their dead parent, each from a very different viewpoint.

Yet there is a barb to this tale, The Branguiel has been hurt so many times that she knows of those who hurt women and she will find them………..
She will hurt them.

Wang Ping
POWER & PITCHFORK--权与权

A German reporter published an article in Daily Mirror to condemn China's violent power around the world. To illustrate her point, she used the character for power to achieve some visual effects. A smart move, for sure. Unfortunately, she picked 杈--pitchfork, for 权--power, and her article, along with the paper, became a laughing stock.

I got curious about the word 权—power. It's definitely a powerful word, a most desired and feared word in English, by its definitions: force, energy, strength, might, right, authority, command, sway, dominion, and by its associations: superpower, powerbroker, manpower, horsepower, evil power, legal power, power of attorney, military power, manipulative power, dependence power, power play, power failure, Macht-politik--political action backed by threats of force, which brings us back to the German reporter's pointed finger at China: use of force.

Her 权 pitchforked a hole through the power 权 she had intended for her essay. I don't know if it's her original intention: to poke a hole into the power, or a Freudian slip: pitchfork, poking through her unverified claims.

I dug into 权's roots. It first appeared in the *Book of Songs* three thousand years ago, as 雚 -- trees budding and flowering in spring, a symbol of life rising from a thawing earth. The word is formed with two images: 木--tree on the left, and 雚--egret on the right. The whole character depicts an egret arriving on a flowering tree from its migration. And both words were carved into the turtle bones as oracles from 4000 years ago, then sang and danced out of poetry together as 雚 —權—权—power.

I can't believe this. I firmly believe this.

So in China, power comes from the earth, as sap returns to trees from roots, pushing out buds, leaves, flowers, spring, for birds arriving from distance, eating insects, resting, nesting and laying eggs in the shade that trees provide.

In Chinese consciousness, power 權 dances in a symbiotic relationship: life helps each, benefits each other, cohabits together.

No wonder Chinese associations with power are 权衡（power balance），权制(power structure)，权智(power wisdom)，权能(power measurement)，and hundreds more.

Power is balanced between dependence and independence, through harmony, through beauty.

And the second meaning of 權, believe it or not, is scale, the balance of all things on earth.

A tree is a master of balance, in order to stand on earth and dance in the wind.

A bird is the best balancer of all, in order to fly, ride air, and land on trees and water.

When two masters dance together, only beauty and poetry can come out of such relationship!

Is this power? I believe it's true power, mightier than super money, superpower, super authority, super law, super weapons like Mother of All Bombs, super politics, Macht-politik.

You're an idiot, Ping, people say. How can a bird, a tree, a scale, let alone a poem, compete with the mightiest authority, law, nuclear bombs, and all other evils on earth?

I say: of all the harsh, violent and ruthless forces related to the word POWER, there's a forgotten word: willpower, preserved for love and beauty.

It is stronger than the hardest metal on earth, mightier than the most destructive weapon man has made, more valuable than all the money the rich can gain, and last longer than any authority, dictatorship, empire.

173

And it's never forgotten, always living inside us, in every form of life, small, yes, hidden, yes, but persistent, automatic, like the heart ticking in our chest, the nucleus in our cell, the mitochondria churning out ATP to keep life alive.

It's invincible, though invisible, and if we grasp our hands together, hold them against our chests, our heartbeats can poke a hole through the black fort of power , turning 权 into a 权, a pitchfork that may point our way back to the origin that has nothing to do with the rights to own or possess--roots for greed and evil, but a true power flowing out of a tree, a flower, an egret, a dance, a song, a poem, that is 權 權

权 quan.

Ron Whitehead
SHOOTIN' UP POETRY IN NEW ORLEANS

Near the levee, a maroon Hudson sedan
driven by Neal Cassady pulls up to a dilapidated old house
with tall grass and weeping willows in the yard.
It's 509 Wagner Street, Algiers, the home of William S. Burroughs.

Neal, Jack Kerouac, Al Hinkle, and LuAnne Henderson arrive,
from the road, to spend a few days with Burroughs.

Burroughs rarely goes out, except to make his connection.
He invites Kerouac to try his "orgone accumulator."

Burroughs says, "Sit inside, and you'll absorb
life-principle atoms right out of the atmosphere."

He attempts to convince Kerouac
into abandoning his road trip with Cassady.

Years later I'm in New Orleans
standing outside The Howlin' Wolf Club.

I'm here to produce
yet another Beat Generation spirited

48-hour non-stop music and poetry INSOMNIACATHON
and I've been burning up the road
day and night with no end in sight.
I'm feelin' burnt out, tired to the bone.

So I'm searchin' for a fix
of poetry to shoot into my blood

to rejuvenate my spirit. I'm calling on Bill Burroughs
and Jack Kerouac and Neal Cassady. But I haven't found my

orgone accumulator my new poetry yet
and my head is hangin' so low it's draggin' the ground.

I've known nothin' but failure lately.

And I've been burnin' the candle at both ends so long

there's nothin' left of me but smoke and ashes.
So I'm wonderin' if the time has finally arrived

for me to become cinder for that long distance
never endin' railroad track to nowhere.

My spirit screams out for help and in a flash
I hear Allen Ginsberg whisper

"Take a hand. Share the word."
And out of the blue

the poetry gospel starts flowin' through
my groin and my gut and my heart and my head.

And my oh my I jump and shout and sing.
Yes, right in front of The Howlin' Wolf Club.

I'm grabbed hold of by the poetry spirit.
And now someone's singin' and bangin' on a piano.
So I open the door and peek in and lo and behold
there's Dr. John doing double-note crossovers

and over and unders. He's doin' his
oola-mala-wala and ZU ZU YA YA.

He's playin' and speakin' in tongues right here
in the middle of the holy New Orleans' afternoon.

And out of the blue I find the poetry I've been lookin' for.
I look up and there's the full moon smilin' at me

from over the Mississippi River and I think of Algiers
and Bill Burroughs and Jack Kerouac and Neal Cassady

and I think of Neal's flame gone gone gone.
His naked body lying beside those

long distance never endin' railroad tracks to nowhere.
And I hope all the poets and musicians

performin' at this 48-hour non-stop
music and poetry INSOMNIACATHON

hell I hope all of us
keep the funk

keep that fuck you flame alive.
Don't let the system break you.
Don't let life break you.
And I hear Dr. John playin' that piano

and singin' his boogie woogie end of the world blues.
And in that moment I know my reward

is in the experience of poetry.
And right here right now I'm in New Orleans

with all these poets and musicians who somehow know
the magical power of poetry.

The word sets us free.
And I think about Allen Ginsberg

and what he said about takin' somebody's hand
cause we're all in this together.

We're pullin'. We ain't pushin'.
We're lettin' it be.

We realize that when one of us is lifted up
we're all lifted up.

And I realize that Poetry is Life
and Life is Poetry.

And I feel an energy risin' through me
growin' strong comin' from poets and musicians of all ages.

And I don't feel like failure anymore.
I feel good. I feel strong.

I feel reborn into Poetry, into Life.
And it feels like resurrection, rebirth.

Rebirth into poetry.
Right here. Right now.

Shootin' up poetry
in New Orleans

Photo page 179 by Jinn Bug

National Beat Poetry Foundation, Inc. Honors

Ron Whitehead
US National Beat Poet Laureate, USA
(2021-2022)

L.J. Talbot
"SALUTING" THE ALABASTER PROGENIES

Hellfire brewing from the
Second Continent…malicious activities.
Fallen out of grace, weakness rises.
Predictability written in treasonous blood.
Triumphantly independent, equality for all!
Our forebears made this country spectacular…
for the White Man.

White Klansman ruins the title
of Dragon and Wizard, turning to
triangular ghosts of disgrace.
Peace in their doll's eyes
involves no color but their own.
To lynch is to be honored.
To maim is to win every war.
White Man's rope hung the hangman
and a karma-laden universe.

White Man in his White House,
sequestered in conspiracy's safety,
endless halls with treacherous rooms.

White 'Murrican' Man flaunts
his patriotism like an Ivy League graduate
with doctorate in hand,
boasting of benefits and the many
joys of segregation, the splendors of
the lack of unresolved issues.
Separate, but equal, but sugarcoated.
White Man's white carpet turns red,
the color of betrayal from 'civil' brothers.

White Textbook Man made
Jesus a glamorous dentine,
lavish robes and biblical aromas.
Every rendition, a fabrication
of a Holy Grail Answer.

The Spear of Destiny impales the carcass of
White Man's previous alter ego.

White Man demands that you
speak the mechanical English language
in a country that was never his to begin with.

Hungry, Hungry Hypocritical White Man turns
his back on the newest families,
arriving with aspirations of their own.
Immigrants of horrific locations,
dictated by those who would murder if questioned.
They plead with waterfalls of sincerity,
but he drives away in a Korean automobile,
wolfing down spiced Pakistani dishes of nourishment.
White Man just remembered where
he placed a great number of Native Americans.

White Man waves his shielding genitalia.
There are but two genders.
You will never change his mind.

White Bread Man stuffs his
face with wholesome artificiality.
Mayonnaise and marshmallow fluff!
White corn tortilla chips and sour cream!
He bathes in ivory soap bubbles,
cleansing his skin with absorbent
microscopic children he released nary an hour ago.
White Man's stomach trampoline is on display through every mirror.

White Man utilizes lethal
gases and increases oven temperatures,
incinerating the roasted flesh of his own class.

White Man with a badge spreads the
honest word that blue lives matter
immediately after gunning down protestors
with the only method of communication
he has known his entire existence.
His breed has made them the enemy since the dawn of sirens.
He is yet another statistic on the Holy Hit List.

White Man is only erect when his firearm is present.

White Man promotes himself,
skinhead ways of life,
the Neo-Con dream of the century.

White Machismo Man extends
the impossible, forbidding white women
to promote white feminism.
Equality for all except the
majority they call 'minorities'.
White Man's nuances wag the decaying tail.
White Man paints a target on the back of every woman.
White Man inquires about what the term 'intersectional' means.

White Man, Heir of Destruction.
White Man inherited a planet of pollution.
White Man inhales pollution to be pessimistically optimistic.

White Settler Man 2.0 enslaves the
rightful owners of the purest lands,
tainting them with rodentia's diseases.
Listen to the White Man's sage words
while raping native women into traumatic oblivion.
He calls them all 'filthy savages'.
White Man's fate, decided by the arrowhead's end.

White Man sings of paradiso.
He should have listened to Lilith.
His burden is his own.

White Man in white collar,
operating his deceased emerald brethren
on numerical paper, privileged above all.
Shuns the impoverished residing
under dank overpasses, begging for half a life.
He is quite charitable towards his investors.
White Man speaks up about his own struggles.

White Whining Man is a staunch
supporter of racial division.
There are great numbers of

ethnic heritage months
because he made all progress possible.
White Man's idea of progress is inevitable defeat.

White Man pays no heed to
the vicissitudes of modern living,
for he was always in the past tense.

White Knight Man defends the
honor of women who wish to speak for themselves.
Bodyguard for the Incels, tormented misfits
whose virginity is a rabid kennel beast.
They spend their funds on deliberate objectification,
to ogle at a dream that remains a magazine photograph.
White Man's superiority complex is small penis energy.

White Man stands alone,
kissing his first world problems
on the reflecting glass lips.

Straight White Man weeps,
pounding sand about how there is
no Straight Day to celebrate,
no Straight Month with soft, grey parades.
White Man does not comprehend acceptance.
White Man, straight and diamond mind mundane.

White Man cries out for
his former alliance,
yet his abandoned principles retaliate.

Abrahamic White Man wants you
to believe in his white deity.
He is welcoming if you join the
mountainous army of chanting followers,
but points a mortal finger of judgment
if you spurn his Lord and Savior.
White Man's finger is now officially broken.

White Man loves his orientation,
yet the rights of humans beyond his
are excluded from his fallen kingdom.

White Food Chain Man endangers
his fellow creatures by means of
bullet kisses and taxidermy trophies.
He deserves his Bald Eagle mascot,
a thief and scavenger by natural trade.
White Man does not discover; his parasitic form
feasts on scraps of original delicacies.

White Man lives his own afterlife,
serving white voices with blackface paint...
Reminder of a world too white for him.

I am an independent river
flowing the other direction.
My alabaster skin is ashamed
to be seen around the lot of you,
mutations of descendants.
A melting pot of curiosities, we ought to be.
A species who is eager to learn,
but the race has reached the finish line.

Dan Wright
A WHOLE LOT OF NOTHING

Whenever I see a familiar face
it is inescapable
that we will ask about
what the other has done
since we last saw each other
Nine times out of ten
the other person will say
"Nothing"

It always strikes me as odd
that people give "Nothing" as an answer so often
and my mind
will always focus on that
as the conversation progresses
I'll imagine this person
just sitting at a table
when they're not at a job or going to bed
contently staring at a wall
If I know they have a partner
and/or kids
I'll imagine them staring at the wall as well
with one of them saying
"Y'know, this really is a nice wall to stare at."

If I haven't seen the person in years
I'll even start to think that that wall
might have something to it
if it was worth being stared at
for years
I'll wonder if I caught them
the one time
they decided to not stare at wall
That they had thought to themselves
earlier in the day
"You know what, maybe there's more to life than this wall!"
But before they go out
they'll pet the wall

to let it know that their going out
is no reflection on the wall

It always makes me wonder
what they consider to be newsworthy
To me, everything is newsworthy
Having a family is newsworthy
A good job is newsworthy
and I say brag about it
if I haven't seen you in forever
But to them, nothing ever is
Even if I know they traveled Europe
for a whole summer
If they performed brain surgery
for the first time
or if they found the secret of eternal life
They would only mention it
if someone else brought it up
by saying something
along the lines of "Yeah, that was a thing."

When the catching up is over,
the pressure of getting on with our day
will get the better of us
and this familiar face and I will both make false declarations
that we need to catch up soon
that neither of us
will want to follow up on
As the truth of it is
both of us
would be so much happier
sitting at home
doing a whole lot of nothing

Rana Zaman
GO OUT ON THE WEEKENDS

Go out leaving supports on the weekends
Keep the encumbrances left having a mouthful water
Take a tolerable bag on the back
Go ahead cutting air with both free hands effortlessly

Go beyond the city to a shady village
There is also growing a lot of urban garbage
Seeing thighs naked don't grab friend!
Leaving the character down, the taste of coffee is also bitter

Everyone needs to know the Azardirachta tree anew
Small fish swim around the duck playing in the pond
The cuckoo's call can be heard suddenly
The joy of finding a nest of weaver birds is endless

The taste of eating in someone's house sitting on the floor is endless!
Until the heartbeat getting normal keep yourself on a bamboo bridge
When the body is sweaty, sniff again and again
And keep taking non-toxic oxygen every moment....

Ewa Maria Zelenay
IMPRESSIONISTS - LITERARY PROGRAM

We are a group of people for whom a word is the beginning of a creative process, which results in further artistic events. We create new forms and kinds, we also mix them. We are inspired by what's the best in every artistic era.

We do not want to criticise or argue with our predecessors. Unlike Futurists, we do not want to escape from the past, we do not want to burn museums, neither do we opt for any upheaval. We do not negate the tradition and we don't approve of anarchy or nihilism. We are not against culture. Under no circumstances do we diminish our predecessors' achievements or conclusions.

We want to base on their discoveries and broaden our horizons with the help of their experience. We don't care about periodization of historical and literary process. What counts for us is actual existing in the history of culture.

With the use of both traditional and contemporary means and techniques, such as: visualisation, hypertext, image and sound – we create impulsive groups. We merge our workshop capabilities into one and they are presented at various events.

We use art, we draw from the art. Impulse makes us look for the perfect ending of the word. A white sheet of paper with a texted written on it, opens and begins our way of experiments.

Surrealists and Dadaists teach us to open our imagination and seek for authenticity, but we don't protest against tradition and realism. Expressionists, on the other hand, teach us how to engage with the presence but without any messianic revolutionism.

We are for freedom in art and we don't want to use any cultural cannibalism. We believe in the broadest sense of cultural osmosis and the term postmodernism we want to fill in real action.

We have gained experience in many areas, but for obvious reasons we cannot be professionals in all fields of art. However, it is not being professional that is the most important for us, but the honesty coming from our impulse.

Painting: Paul Cézanne, Trees and Houses Near the Jas de Bouffan

Catherine Zickgraf
EMERGE

You left the week the woods took my man cat.
They swallowed him, gone among the trees
of leaves like waves of windy seas.

I write on my balcony, where you never sat—
my widow's walk, where the tree coasts surge.
You dove in forest and never emerged.

Nothing is forever. I know you're not coming back.
I was often at the crossroads waiting to choose.
Now I choose to heal the soul you bruised.

I'm stronger than you know though I'm lacking you,
though you found my depths and curled in my bed,
nuzzled my neck then left me for dead.

Catherine Zickgraf
OLD EYES

Even my irises are going gray.
Doc says I may lose my pigment.
They're green as summer leaves,
so I don't want to believe it.

But I have old eyes, I struggle.
Inner lids reject contacts.
Face spasms reject glasses.
Surgery didn't quite take.

Vision is pain. Sometimes
I sense the world approach.
But mostly I live invisibly since
I cannot see you seeing me.

Published at *NEW YORK PARROT*
Literary Corner

The Poet Transfigured by Dustin Pickering

John Copley Alter
YAHRZEIT, FRAGMENT

September now is burdened with yahrzeit.
My grandmother
turns well into her third century.
My childhood
friend turns seventy-four. Our war
against Islam
turns nineteen. And you, my brother,
has it been three years
since you held in your strong hands
a cricket
bat? Indifferent to history
the season
turns, but the football
pitch is silent. Autumn
leaves will fall on empty stadiums.
History harvests aristocracies.
Who speaks Latin
anymore? Time
Passes.

Rupsingh Bhandari
HIMALAYAS' MORNING

Every Morning
When Himalayas gives birth
To sun without screaming
Bleeding panoramically
In the heady height of whiteness
The shadow fades away from me and
Sings...the silent song of mystery
I also inflame
In the celebration of creation....every morning
Little by little disappear
As incense ashes
On the altar of Himalayas.

The reflected redness from Himalayas
Every tree uses as lipstick
Without any hesitations
The ravines and the group of clouds
Surrender without any complains in to the serene gorge of
Adolescent River...
Birds enliven in branches...carrying the
Immense destination in their tiny wings.
Sky stretches throughout the meadows carpeted by wild flowers
Breeze thickens by Himalaya's warmth
Slows its secret patrolling.

I also float as the dandelion seeds
Being into pieces one by one
Far away from within
Every morning
I lose myself little by little and become Himalayas
When Himalayas gives
Birth to sun without screaming
Bleeding panoramically
In the heady height of whiteness.

Dr. Piku Chowdhury
HOW LONG WOULD YOU HIDE?

How you hide in holes !
In anonymity and obscurity,
Locking doors and blocking the zones
That you dare not face anymore.
Perhaps ravines of guilt and shame
Or some fear that haunts but fails
To be defined in contours clear,
make you crouch in private cells
And guard your life like fawns and quails
Endangered by public gaze
 And seamless depths of indifference.
Strange perplexity of warring wishes,
Incognito in existence;
Social stages you must cling to
yet the humans frighten too -
Resist you must against the floods
with such helpless embankments.
What if floods just crush your gate
Bring you face to face with fate,
Despairingly you sigh and regret
That for sturdier locks its late;
Will you shrivel in glare of truth
Shredding the mask of hurt innocence?
Will you stand then bare and cold
In the gaze of a long-lost soul
That no longer feels or dreams
But stares beyond all loss or gain.
Will you fear the vacuity,
That would greet your existence?

Nandita De *nee* Chatterjee
BENEDICTION

Between us and God
Constant pleas
Humble prayers for forgiveness
Countless trespasses of mankind
Unconscious of consequences.

Now on our knees
A world begging for benediction
Striving for reform
Introspecting on fallacies
A planet wronged mercilessly
By savage people.

Now hapless in the apathy
Penitent and powerless
An entire people in prayers
The only hope that remains
For salvation of mankind.

Neil Desmond
"THIS IS IT"

"Thanks for having me over," Ron Jakes offered as he sat down at the kitchen table. Harold Wilkins, a fellow police officer, put a bottle of beer down on the table before his guest.

"I don't know how you do it, Ron. Being a part time reverend in addition to being a cop. You must be very busy," the host observed.

"Well, I don't have a wife and kids yet," the younger and newer officer noted in response. "Where are your wife and kids, anyway? I was hoping to see those little tykes tonight."

"She's got them in the other room. In front of the T. V., I'm sure. You see, Rev., there's something specific I wanted to talk to you about. Something I didn't want the wife and kids hearing about," Harold explained.

"Oh, I see. What is it?"

"Well, I noticed that some of the bro's on the force look up to you, even though you've only been a cop for a few years. You communicate pretty well, and you have integrity." Harold paused to take a sip of his own beer. "So I got to thinking. We've got a problem on this force. You know that right?"

"What kind of problem?"

"Thugs. Good ol' boys. Racists. Power trip guys."

"Well, that's true, Harold. But doesn't every big city department have those. Look at what happened in Minneapolis," Ron observed.

"I know, Rev. Most departments have this problem. But things have changed since Minneapolis. They should have changed long before that, but they didn't. It's different this time, though. The good white cops are talking about it now, too. Most of them used to say nothing about bad cops. They were like two separate camps who avoided each other and stayed out of each other's business, as much as they could, anyway. Whenever a bro would bring it up with one of the straight-laced white guys, it was always the same type of answer. It was always, 'I don't like that scumbag either, but cops can't turn on cops. We have to have each other's back out on the street.' Well, they're not saying that anymore."

Both of Ron's eyebrows raised in response, causing lines to appear on his forehead. The twenty-eight-year-old raised his bottle and took a swill. "Okay, what are they saying?"

"They've started to say things like, 'something's got to change,' and 'those scumbags are bringing whole departments down with them.' Stuff like that. Nothing specific in terms of ideas, but myself and other bros have definitely noticed a change in their responses."

"Okay, so now's the time to make some sort of move? Is that what you're saying? And you want me to be involved?"

"Yes, Rev. In fact, it's not just a matter of you being involved. You're the best man to take this to the higher ups. I've heard a couple of your sermons, Rev. You have the ability to move people, emotionally. This is an important moment. It's an important time for the department, and for law enforcement in general. We need a voice like yours to be a liaison between the good cops and the higher ups. A problem like this is not going to be solved from the outside. Politicians aren't going to fix this the right way. This has to be solved from the inside," Harold asserted.

The young reverend sat back in his chair. He let go of his bottle and folded his arms on his chest.

"This is a tough thing, isn't it? Getting from here to there isn't going to be easy," Ron deduced.

"I'm sure it won't be, Rev. That's why I'm asking you. You'll have to bring your 'A game,' but I think you can do it."

"Well, I've got one thing on my side. The Chief is a bro."

"It's not the Chief you need to talk to," Harold advised, to Ron's surprise.

"What do you mean?" Ron wondered aloud. He was beginning to realize things were not as they seemed in the department.

"The Chief may be a bro, but he's also a politician, in a sense. You don't get to be Chief in this city without making some deals. Sweeping some things under the rug. Owing some favors."

The two men fell silent as Harold's wife, Geraldine, entered the kitchen. "Sorry to interrupt. I've got to get some water for little Harold. He keeps saying he's thirsty. How are you, Ron? That was a fine sermon you gave on Sunday."

"Well, thank you. How are you and the kids?"

Geraldine was waiting for the glass to fill up with water from the kitchen sink. "I don't even understand what they are watching in there. Something about gladiators with superpowers. I can't even follow it. Anyway, good to see you, Ron."

After Geraldine exited from the kitchen, Ron turned his attention back to Harold. "Well, who do I have to talk to, then?"

"I think the only guy who can really coordinate this thing is Royce."

Ron again looked surprised. "Royce? Detective in Homicide? He's working a high profile case right now. Besides, he's white. Why would he stick his neck out for us?"

"They say he's something of a maverick…" Harold began.

"Oh, that's right," Ron countered, somewhat skeptically. "I heard about this. He insisted on body cameras while the rank and file opposed them. It turns out he was right, so now he's some sort of maverick. Is that it?"

"Something like that. But look, the guy's got cred, okay? Not just on the street, but he's got cred with the higher ups, too. The Chief has to listen to him because he can go above the Chief. He can go to the Mayor and the Mayor will listen. He's a name, a somebody. And if a concrete plan develops here, he can get the higher ups on board."

"Well, Harold. What's the goal here, if we do get a concrete plan? What's the punch line?"

Harold took another swill of his beer, without breaking eye contact with his guest.

"To axe the thugs. To get them off the force for good. That's the goal."

****

Officers Mike Dickey and Sean Harris were having a game of pool in Dickey's "man cave" type basement. Beer and pool had occupied much of their spare time since the pandemic started. No sports to watch, no bars or movie theaters to go to. For the two officers in their late twenties, it was an unconventional time. For them, it was about pool, beer and "shop talk."

"Well, about how old was that moolie, anyway?"

Mike was asking his fellow officer about a "takedown" type of arrest he'd executed in Precinct 19 the week before.

"I guess he was about our age," Sean supposed. "He seemed a little confused. Confused about who was in charge…about who was calling the shots. So I schooled him on that."

"I hate when they forget who's who during an arrest," Mike offered as he put chalk on the tip of his pool stick. "Those people over in Precinct 19, it's like they think we wear these uniforms because it's Halloween. How many times you had take a suspect down over that way, anyhow?"

"You mean how many moolies did I take down?" Sean asked, now using the chalk himself.

"Yeah, that's what I mean," Mike clarified.

"Who knows? You lose track after a bit. I think I took down four back in April. There was about one per week for a while there."

****

Officer Ron Jakes had met Detective Dennis Royce on a couple of occasions. He knew of some basic information about the detective. He knew that Royce's wife had died a few years earlier, and he lived alone. Royce was in his fifties and had no children. He was an army veteran. He had solved an important, high profile murder case a few years prior. And then there was his "claim to fame" – his insistent advocacy for body cameras, which had once put him at odds with the rank and file. Further, there was one more bit of information Ron had picked up along the way: the detective liked Guinness.

****

"These are strange times, aren't they Dennis? No sports to watch, no bars to go to…'

"Oh, hello, Jakes." The detective appeared surprised to find the junior officer near his locker, or in his part of the complex at all, for that matter.

"There's something I've got to talk to you about. It's important, and we can't have an audience. Would you be open to stopping by my place after work tonight? It won't take long, and I have a six pack of Guinness."

The detective was looking into his locker and appeared to be fishing around for something. "Well, I can't turn that down," he replied. Finally, he located the tie he'd been searching for. Turning back to Ron, he inquired, "Where's your place again?"

****

"Okay, Reverend, what's this all about? Why did you invite me over?" Royce wondered aloud as he sat at the junior officer's kitchen table, Guinness in hand.

"Well, Detective. There's a thorny issue that's got to be dealt with. I've spoken quietly with a number of officers about it. We believe you are best positioned to effectively deal with it. You are respected from the Mayor's office on down, and that's what we're going to need to get this done."

"All right, then, what do you got?"

"Well, Detective, it's about bad cops. Every city of this size has them and we have them, too. After Minneapolis, indeed, after Ferguson, we believe a different approach to these guys is necessary."

Royce sipped the stout and offered his opinion on the issue. "We've tried to get those guys to go straight before. They say the right things at the right time and then they go back to their old ways. You can't fix stupid."

"I know, Detective. That's why we want to change our approach. We don't want to get them to go straight anymore. We want to get rid of them altogether. We want them off the force for good."

The detective's eyes widened as he straightened up and sat back in his chair. A globe above the kitchen table provided light between the two men. Detective Royce took a deep breath. "Well, that's easier said than done. The problem is that excessive force is hard to prove, unless there's a video of it, like in Minneapolis. That's why I wanted body cameras. The officer always says that the suspect was resisting…"

"Resisting, getting violent, creating a hazardous situation…I know. We've all heard it before," Ron replied, concluding the detective's thought. "We get that. But here's what we're thinking. We know who the punks are on this force. All of the good cops know who they are. If we give you that list, you could take it to the Chief. Don't worry, we'll sniff out personal vendettas and keep that stuff off the list. Only the true scumbags will make the list. Only the names that keep coming up over and over again. The Chief can go through their personnel files and find something on them. Maybe they said the wrong thing to a female employee at one point. Maybe there's a technicality somewhere. Maybe they made a mistake on an expense form. Maybe they took a cruiser just outside the jurisdiction by accident one night. Then he can fire them."

"Whoa…whoa…wait a minute," the detective interrupted, putting both hands up as if stopping a car at a traffic checkpoint. "You want me to sell this to the Chief? You're talking about doing an end run around the city's contract with the police union. You'll be setting the city up for one wrongful termination lawsuit after another. The Chief's not going to go for that, and neither will the Mayor."

Ron had anticipated he'd run into informed resistance from Detective Royce. Yet, when it surfaced, it still rattled his confidence for a moment.

The reverend took a deep breath, then regained his composure. He realized Harold had been right about needing to bring his "A- game."

"Hear me out, Detective. The lawsuits would come after the thugs had been fired and were no longer on the force. Nine good cops have already given me their word that they will testify against those punks once they are no longer cops. They will tell the courts and administrative boards what they've witnessed these thugs doing out on the street. Detective, everything has changed since Minneapolis. We can make it stick this time. We have to, Detective. Bad cops are dragging the name of good cops through the mud. They are dragging the name of the whole profession, all of law enforcement, through the mud. They are dragging our legacy through the mud."

Ron noticed a slow change in Royce's demeanor. The look on his face appeared more serious, more contemplative. Ron continued as the detective brought a bottle of Guinness to his lips.

"It's got to stop. We can't kick this can down the road anymore. There's no more road left to kick it down. We've just reached a point in time when it's no longer enough to be a good cop. This is one of those moments history when we have to be great cops. We have to step up to greatness. This is it. We have to take on the bad cops, not just the bad guys on the street. Whether it's fair that it's falling to us or not, that's just the hand history has dealt us."

The two men looked at each other silently for a few seconds. Ron noticed the detective's adams apple, which was prominent, move up and down in his throat.

"Reverend," Royce began in a low voice.

"Yes?" the junior officer replied.

The detective looked away, towards his right, and took a deep breath. He then turned back towards Ron. "A couple of these guys aren't only thugs," he advised. "They're downright crazy. Going after them could put our lives on the line."

Ron's eye brows rose, again causing lines on his forehead. His hands turned the glass of beer in front of him around in slow circles.

"That may be true, Detective. But remember a few months back, when this pandemic started to hit?"

"Yes," Royce answered, one eye brow raised.

"Those medical people, they were called upon to step up, even at risk to their own lives. They didn't bargain for that, but it was the hand history had dealt them. There was no one else who could do it, the public had nowhere else to turn. They had to step up to the moment, and they did. They stepped up to greatness. Now history has dealt us the same hand."

Again, the two men looked at each other in silence. Ron noticed the detective's face had turned slightly to the left, yet his eyes continued their locked on eye contact. His stare and clenched jaw line made for a striking image under the globe light. Ron wondered briefly if the detective's face had adopted the same expression when he'd resolved to advocate for body cameras, years earlier.

"I'll do it," the detective said.

****

"So that's the situation, Chief. Everything's changed since Minneapolis. If part of the apple is rotten, then the whole apple is rotten. What happened in Minneapolis could happen here," pleaded Detective Royce. He was concluding his pitch to Chief James Adams, a pitch that had included a concrete game plan, and had been going on for over thirty minutes.

"I don't know, we're talking about lawsuit after lawsuit here…" The Chief's wariness did not come as a surprise to the twenty-five year veteran of the force. He knew he had to press on. He also knew that he – and only he – could go above the Chief if he had to. He didn't want to do so, but he'd given Officer Jakes his word he would do whatever he had to to get this done.

"If we have to settle a couple of those suits out of court, then we can do so this time. We can do it because the public will be behind the firings this time. Even the *corporate public* will be behind us this time. They just want the bad cops off the force. That's all they want. They just want the punks out."

"Well, it seems like you've thought this through, Detective. Let me ask you something. Did you think the fact that I'm black would make me more likely to go in one direction or another on this? Is that what you thought?"

The chief's question struck Royce as quite different than any question he'd been asked in his career, perhaps even in his life. It was as if the Chief were prying into his subconscious, to see what was there. Because Royce himself did not know with certainty what was there, he found himself in something of a mental pickle. He was like a baseball player caught in a run down between first and second base. But this notion only delayed the detective's response momentarily.

"No, Chief. It's not like that, I just think we've got a problem here and it's going to blow up in our face if we don't fix it," he replied, in an uncharacteristically humble tone.

Throughout Detective Royce's pitch, the Chief had been sitting forward in his chair, his elbows on his desk. Now he reclined back in his chair, moving his arms onto its arm rests. A smile came over his face. "This job's a pain in the ass. You were smart not to take it when you had the chance," he observed, chuckling.

The Chief's observation, as well as the change in his demeanor, had a defusing effect and lightened the mood in the room considerably. Royce moved in his chair, placing his elbows on his knees, and leaned forward so he could look down at the floor as he chuckled and nodded in agreement with the observation. "I figure as much," he replied.

The Chief continued his light - hearted lamentations. "The Mayor's a closet drunk, you know that, right?" his chuckle elevating to a laugh.

"I'd heard a rumor or two," the detective acknowledged as he continued chuckling and nodding while looking between his legs towards the floor.

"It's always the same thing with the city council. 'Why did you pay so much for those uniforms? Why did you buy that cruiser? What was wrong with the other one? We don't have money for this!' It's just the same crap all the time."

The sense of merriment caused by the Chief's humorous musings had escalated to the point where both men were laughing at the thankless nature of their respective positions on the force. The anxiety Royce had felt only moments before seemed like a distant memory. But then, suddenly, he felt it returning. It occurred to him that the room had now gone completely silent. He quickly looked up at the Chief.

Chief Adams' demeanor had, once again, changed drastically in what seemed like an instant. He almost appeared to be glaring at the detective, as if his eyes were piercing through Royce rather than at him. His teeth were clenched. The profound and sudden change in the Chief's expression startled the seasoned detective.

"Put that list together," Chief Adams said, in a 'direct order' tone of voice. "Bring me the names of the punks."

THREE WEEKS LATER

"Why were those six police officers fired, Chief?"

Chief Adams had been approached by a local radio reporter and a sound technician as he exited city hall and descended the concrete steps which connected the street to its front doors.

"They lied on expense forms or time sheets," he replied, curtly.

"They say those were minor, accidental errors, Chief. They say they're going to challenge this through the union. They say they are going to file wrongful termination suits against the department."

"They can file anything they want, but they are no longer members of this police department, and they're not going to be again. Excuse me, gentlemen, I've got to get back to the station," the Chief advised as he entered a car waiting at the curb.

****

Officers Mike Dickey and Sean Harris were once again playing pool in Mike's basement.

"Hey Mike," Sean began as he cued up his pool stick.

"What?"

"Those firings that happened the other day, they were kind of out of the blue, don't you think?"

"So what?" Mike's contributions to the conversation were being produced between gulps from a beer bottle.

"Well," Sean continued, "Do you think they really got fired because they filled forms out wrong? I mean, do you think that's the real reason?"

"Sure it is. That's what they said over at city hall, isn't it?"

"Well, I know that's what they *said*, but I'm starting to question it. Did you notice all six of them were enforcer type cops, like us?"

"I did notice none of them were moolies. And now that you mention it, I suppose all those guys were enforcers, yes." Mike managed to take a shot on the table between swigs of beer and the reluctant responses he was granting to Sean's observations.

Sean applied chalk to his stick's tip as he continued the conversation, "Well, I've also heard rumors."

"Rumors?" Mike replied immediately, one eyebrow raised.

"Yeah, supposedly this is just the start. More firings are coming down and it won't be long. Some of the names I've heard getting thrown around are enforcers, also. Our brand of enforcer, I mean. I haven't heard your name or mine yet, but I'm starting to get worried about this. No straight-laced cops have been mentioned. No 'by the book' guys. I think the 'forms' story is just a cover. I think there's a broader agenda here." He then took a shot, knocking a ball into a hole.

Mike applied chalk to the end of his stick, but said nothing.

Sean, surprised by Mike's silence, pressed further. He was hoping perhaps he was just being paranoid. He was hoping Mike would tell him so, that he was just being paranoid. "What do you think, Mike?"

Mike took a shot, knocking his ball in a hole. "I think we'd better straighten our laces and keep them straight," he said.

****

Officer Ron Jakes fished through his locker, certain he'd left his water bottle there earlier. Officer Harold Wilkins arrived, opening his locker next to Ron's.

"Well, Reverend. Seems like things are changing fast around here," he noted with a smile on his face.

Ron smiled himself as he continued his search for the water bottle. "Indeed they are," he concurred.

Harold's curiosity was getting the better of him. "Okay, Rev, seriously. How'd you do it? How did you get the old boxer to go back in the ring for one more bout?"

Officer Jakes chuckled as he finally emerged with the water bottle, like a gold prospector who'd found his treasure at the bottom of the sand.

"Well," the Reverend noted, good naturedly. "He lets his guard down if you can get a Guinness or two in him."

#Minneapolis by Dustin Pickering

Stephen Ditmore

IS ZION IN THE CARIBBEAN?

[Genesis 13 with a modern cast of characters]

Lin-Manuel Miranda, his family and close friends, were on a working vacation in the Dominican Republic when Lin's collaborator, Quiara Hudes, brought him a message. "Wyclef Jean wants to meet with you." she said, referring to the Haitian musician.

"Sure, have him come over."

"He wants to bring 400 friends & family, and he wants to meet at the Haitian border."

Lin-Manuel took a deep breath, and let it out slowly. It was a bold & intrusive request, seemingly out-of-the-blue; but Lin-Manuel, the dramatist, couldn't say no. "Let's make it a camping trip, then." A date was set, and when the time came Lin-Manuel ventured out with nearly 100 colleagues, friends and family.

After driving to Jimani the party hiked southwest, toward the border along the Rio Blanco, pitching their tents about halfway. Lin, though a gregarious type, occasionally liked some time alone, and pitched his tent away from the others, across the river.

In the night an angel appeared in the form of Felice Leon of The Root. "Look at me, Lin-Manuel," said the angel. "Under this beautiful dark exterior I'm pulsating pink, just like you. I don't see myself reflected in your work, though."

"The *In The Heights* movie's done, I can't remake it now," protested Lin-Manuel. "I'll try to do better next time." Then he added, without meaning to say his next thought, "Who are you, and why don't you go back where you came from?"

"You mean Cuba?" asked the angel. "Maybe I will. Or maybe," she said archly, "I'll bring Cuba to Nuevo York."

"That's your business" said Lin, wishing she'd leave. "Who are you to be up in mine?"

"I'll show you your business," said the angel, and the two wrestled, a long, difficult fight, with many reversals. At last Lin had the upper hand, pinning the angel to the ground.

"Tell me your name," Lin-Manuel demanded.

"I am that I am," said the angel. "Now get off me, you big oaf!" Lin slowly rose and shook himself off. "You're as thick as your ticket lines are long, aren't you," said the Angel. "I grew up right down the street from you, and yet I'm invisible."

"Hardly," panted Lin, exhausted by the fight, "You've had your say, and it's been widely reported. Isn't that enough? I'm not the worst culprit."

"Open your eyes, Lin-Manuel," said the angel, "this isn't over yet," and with an expert sweep of her legs worthy of *Crouching Tiger, Hidden Dragon*, Lin was flat on his back with the angel's foot on his pelvis and his leg in her hands, at which point she expertly dislodged his thigh from its socket. "When they ask you why you're limping, tell them I was here," she said. "By the way, your name is Israel."

"What ..?" ask Lin, "I don't get it."

"You don't get much, do you," said the angel. With that, she was gone.

In the morning tents were broken down, and after breakfast the party set out on foot, checking a GPS for the latitude & longitude provided by Wyclef. The supplies they brought were considerable, but no one asked questions when Lin-Manuel unexpectedly asked others to carry his share. Lin walked with his sister, Luz.

"What is the point of all this, Lin? Luz asked after a time. "Some guy sends a mysterious message out of the blue, and you drag us all to the middle of nowhere?"

"You know I like history. There's history here, and we're chasing it."

"You're not chasing anything limping like that," Luz pointed out. What's the problem?

"I am that I am," began Lin.

"That'll surprise no one," said Luz, "but it doesn't explain the limp."

Lin-Manuel Miranda stopped, drew a deep breath and looked at his sister. "Look, if we're talking 500 people, we need to get there and start the cooking fires. There needs to be plenty for everyone, and I'm off the pace this morning. Why don't you and the others go ahead of me?" As she left, Lin-Manuel quietly finished his thought; "I am that I am is a bitch-and-a-half."

By the time Lin-Manuel hobbled to the border, cooking was underway on both sides. Wyclef spotted him, raced to Lin and gave him a great hug. "Welcome, Brother!" he boomed, like he was James Earl Jones, looking Lin square in the face, a hand on each of Lin's triceps. "I'm so glad you are here," he then breathed in a gentler tone.

Lin was relieved at the warm welcome; so relieved that his knees nearly buckled as tension in his body gave way. He recognized, at that moment, that while he had been putting on a brave face, he had been scared. Initiating a second embrace, he hugged Wyclef. As he stepped back, his bad leg nearly gave way. Wyclef held him up, then came alongside him, under his arm. "What is wrong?" asked Wyclef as an involuntary tear ran down Lin's face. "Are you hurt?"

"Everyone wants something from me, Wyclef," said Lin-Manuel with honest emotion. "But in your case, could be I owe you. I was listening to The Fugees as I got started."

"Pffff, there's a lot of history, brother," said Wyclef, gesturing dismissively with his one free hand. After carefully sitting on mossy rocks, Wyclef continued in a quiet, personal tone. "Look where we're sitting. You're always trying to connect shit back to the Caribbean. The American Revolution wasn't the only one, you know."

"I know, I know." But even as he said it, he recalled the angel's words: 'You don't know much, do you.'

"Yeah, this place has a history," said Wyclef. It could have a future, too. "What'cha gonna do when you get to Zion, Mr. Israel?" asked Wyclef.

"How'd you know about that?"

"Word travels fast on this island. You must be hungry." Wyclef gestured, and like the Red Sea converging after earlier being parted, the two entourages converged bearing plates of food for one-another with joyous greetings.

When the two realized they were on the Haitian side of the border, Lin asked Wyclef to eat with him. The two crossed the few steps back to D.R. "Are we supposed to do this?" Lin asked.

"Not everyone can, brother," said Wyclef, "but you and I, we got the passports."

Bernard Haske
CLEAN

LIVE!
from New York,
deliver
the 5 lb. human
for the ritual
neck snap,
that human
touch,
the clean, smooth
piercing –
all it will know,
feel,
bleed

Pavol Janik
NEW YORK (British English)

In a horizontal mirror
of the straightened bay
the points of an angular city
stabbing directly into the starry sky.

In the glittering sea of lamps
flirtatious flitting boats
tremble marvelously
on your agitated legs
swimming in the lower deck
of a brocade evening dress.

Suddenly we are missing persons
like needles in a labyrinth of tinfoil.

Some things we take personally –
stretch limousines,
moulting squirrels in Central Park
and the metal body of dead freedom.

In New York most of all it's getting dark.

The glittering darkness lights up.

The thousand-armed luster of the mega city
writes Einstein's message about the speed of light
every evening on the gleaming surface of the water.

And again before the dusk the silver screen
of the New York sky floods
with hectoliters of Hollywood blood.

Where does the empire of glass and marble reach?
Where do the slim rackets of the skyscrapers aim?

God buys a hot dog
at the bottom of a sixty-storey street.

God is a black
and loves the grey color of concrete.

His son was born from himself
in a paper box
from the newest sort of slave.

Ljubica Katic
DISAPPEAR, KORONA

Desolate cities looking like ghosts,
Victims are still dropping dead in their tracks
From this ferocious plague going around the world.
God save all the people from this calamity.

Why is this korona venom spreading,
Whose experiments are these,
When will all this calm down and cease?
People are living in fears.

The world's getting covered in pain, suffering, and tears,
The fears for your loved ones bring no peace;
This plague chooses neither the old nor young ones.
It has united us all into one flock.

God, if you exist,
Save us from these troubles.
Give us the hope of our salvation, reach out to us.
Protect every human being,
Let the sun shine on the earth.

Wansoo Kim
LET'S GO TO DRIVE OUT THE ROTTEN RIVER WATER

Those who look at the river
Folding their hands behind their back,

Even if they hurl abuses,
Spit,
And turn their back,
The rotten river water won't disappear by itself.

When all of us plunge into the rotten river water
And become a strong current
With the hearts where the blood of the holy anger
And the fervent prayer seethe,
The rotten river water will move back.

Let's go unfolding our hands behind our back
And plunge into the river.
If you and I don't do so,
The rotten river water won't disappear by itself.

Andre de Korvin
REST EASY GOOD CITIZENS

This is not a call
to revolution,
not a call
to take up arms.

It's the man who watches
boats drift on the river
all day long.
The man who woke today,

tired of hearing
the myth of hard times now
and good times coming.
Tired of seeing day after day

the stock ticker
zigging and zagging its way
through fog shrouded crystal balls.
The man who watches boats,

and has no shoes, wants to expose
the lies, to tell It
like it is.
Tell It like it is

to the people, the leaders
the drifters, the supreme court
to people like him that have no shoes.
The great A+ dream, he starts,

the A+ dream,
not A+ for everyone.
Not A+ for the working poor
sinking below the line,

the unemployed, for those who live
in substandard houses,
who live in tents, subways
and under bridges
and who don't want to live.

Not A+ for laid-off people,
those with part time jobs
and no benefits,

the 40 plus million
with no health
and no dental insurance.
The man who watches boats

wants to scream
but it's not for him alone
he wants to scream.
He wants to scream for all

those too tired to speak,
for those who watch boats
and have no shoes.
The dream not A+

for the elderly whose daily choice is
food or medication,
who eat cat food,
dog food, who don't eat,

women who can't get maternity leaves.
Not A+ for those with heat cut off
in the middle of winter,
who die on sweltering summer days

because they can't pay the rent,
who have no phone, no id,
those afraid to apply for foodstamps
welfare and Medicaid,

the million and a half who filed
for bankruptcy last year.
Not A+ for illegal aliens
working as slaves in sweatshops,

shotguns pressed against their heads.
Not A+ for those
working 70 hours a week
by their employer's dictate,

forced to pay more and more of
their insurance and pension costs,
who live in reservations,
who live in ghettos,

who live in cars.
Not A+ for those walking the streets
because they have no place to go,
who have come to the dead

end of their lives,
who can't wait to die.
The man who watches boats
and has no shoes

screams there would be beauty
in red flames lovingly kissing
the walls of every police station,
making them blush scarlet.

Beauty, he screams,
in the 80 foot chimney
crashing on roofs of federal buildings,
beauty in a herd of unicorns charging

windows of downtown banks.
Beauty in the big bang carrying
Wall Street in small pieces
to the four corners of the world.

Caroline Laurent Turunc
TRAVELER OF THE ROADS

Neither the dagger nor the knife could have bled so much
A drop of nostalgia between existence and nothingness that is often seen
Then we put the smell of pain instead of kohol
And the sadness of the swelling in the cheek ditch

The harness had no tongue, the Ruby the Emerald were diamonds!
Even though the truth had a name we called it
Knot, beggar, drunk
We cut off the finger of the one who reaches out

unknown of the time who created the creator!
Who are the poorest in existence and in nothingness
Are they those who lack morals or rich in goods?
Or is it the stalk of the ear of wheat pitting us against each other?
Give birth to kill hide.

Was this the end point of the most precious advice
On top of the one who knows eloquence and rhetoric by heart
Cry those who observes neither the rhyme nor the measure nor the style
Imperialism that have taken the continent under its influence is a reptile
Is it for the meal of the wolves all these joys all these cries of pain

These wolves have known sheep for millions of centuries
They discovered the tastiest pearl in the throat
Those who are like us belong to them to the bone
Serve throat food for their hundreds
Rubies were children's tears

O wayward traveler in the desert of Kaaba
The wound of ignorance is not the sun of science
The sun is hard work for the earth to reach
And you, oh son of man unbelieving religion, morals, faith were very
expensive
But you, you sold them at a low price

Sudipta Maity
 # PIECE OF LIFE #

The outcome of the war
Begins cutting game
Machines' sound breaks the ears
Of the forest dwellers
Trees have to remain silent
For fear of pruning
Forest life suffering
In the dark eyes of
Money loss
The fireflies are spreading Darkness
Life is used to burn dead people.

Navneet K. Maun
THE EARTH IS NOT OURS TO POSSESS

In the rear balcony
I beheld a fat, tabby cat
stretched out regally, luxuriously
basking in the sun,
a smug look, licking its whiskers.
Alas, my premonition was correct
It had gobbled up a pigeon,
A mere fledgling,
for the feathers scattered around
were few and soft looking.
I recoiled at the brutality.
My voice of reason whispered
It is the Survival of the fittest.
The spectre of a nuclear holocaust
hangs over humanity
like the sword of Damocles
threatening mass obliteration.
Martyrdom at what cost?
The kith and kin condemned
to a life of emotional incumbrance.
The pestilence of war
comes and retreats like waves
lulling the senses
fanning false hopes.
Mans' obsession for land
perennial since antiquity.
Why must the Nations big or small
be jaundiced, covetous?
Considering their tenure on Earth so brief.
The recent Pandemic has expounded
The sanctity of life.
Mother Earth needs to heal too,
her flora and fauna recuperate
to prevent a Wasteland.
After all, how much land
does a Coffin occupy
when a person is reduced to dust.

James B. Nicola
OTHERWISE, OR, INCLUSIVE TERMINOLOGY

An erstwhile "colored person" *explains why*
more recent labels do not satisfy

Please don't call me *Of Color*, which
is assonant with *The Other*,
which I am not. I'm only rich
of hue to you, my brother.

Nor shall I call you *White* which rhymes
with *bright, might, right*, and *light*.
You're nowhere white, and oftentimes
so far from right or bright.

Call me *Of Worldwide Ancestry*,
then: accurate and true.
What's more, while it refers to me,
it might as well mean you.

Or would you now prefer to be
called *ashen, pale, off-pink*...?
Then you'd be the minority,
though. Rightly so, you think?

Tu Niu
A FARMER'S HOMELAND

A farmer's homeland, is gathered in his palm of land
He never walks out of the crop line of sight, for his lifelong
Harvests of blossom in spring and fruit in autumn

A farmer's sweat permeates into soil, unnoticed, so –
It never stops pouring, that his piece of land
Is neither thirsty nor barren
A farmer's power is small, so –
He plows, hoes, and shoulders his rice
That his homeland is full of vigor at all times

The loud sounds of chant
Echo in the sky, so rivers and mountains
Are immersed in excitement
That they can't hold back their great joy
A farmer's intention
Never stays overnight, so he works until dawn
To uproot weeds that prevent his aspiration

A farmer's homeland is narrow, so –
He defends its territory: a village, and a few ridges
That he persists across generations, and
Keeps fostering his daughters and sons
How vast a farmer's homeland!
The Map of Rooster, hung high on the wall, daily patrolling
Records a farmer's footprints on his homeland

Ngozi Olivia Osuoha
MYSTERY

I wonder deep and get lost
As I wander far and via off
I derail and fail down the rail
Moving slowly like the snail
Yet get soaked in the rain of pain.

I cannot comprehend life
Events torment me to the bones
Circumstances drill me dry
Situations drag me in the mud
Conditions pull my muscles
I cry in fear and weep in wear
As mysteries throw us up and down.

Morals have become traps
Principles have turn delays
Self-discipline is now a grave
And self-control a disqualification,
I don't understand life
I can't comprehend mysteries
People take advantage of the meek.

No wonder majority follow the bandwagon
No wonder they turn a madding crowd
And create animal kingdoms
If that would take them to stardom
Or cure their boredom.

Help me, hold my hand
Let my head not covered in sand
Nor my face buried in shame
Let my feet aright, alright, rightly stand.

Monalisa Parida
FOREST IS IN DANGER

Fire!
Extreme destruction and devastation!
From grass to bush
From bush to tree
Trees after tree
So widely it runs.
Flames leaping to the sky.
The sky is crying blood and loud.
With sleepless weary eyes.
The night is pained.
The moon and stars are red.
Forest is burning
Mother nature is shocked
Stands aloof and stunned
Like a mother waits
Outside the ICU.
With a hope of rain.
Wild animals all losing homes
Running helter-skelter
Like leaves of the west wind.
But mankind sleeps
With a deep sleep
Unaware and careless.

Elina Petrova
PILOT TALES

i Surnames of Birds

A few coworkers in our mid-thirties, we drove
from our walled factory to a desolate airdrome –
to jump with parachutes after a brief training.
For a predictably doomed office romance I had
to nip in the bud, a parachute for *Brüderschaff**
seemed to serve as a right setting. But first
we wanted to try flexwing microlights.

A grizzled pilot glanced at the tweed on my boss,
at my chiffon blouse, and brought me his fleece.

Scolding-cold October in the heights…
Fields decreased in size, tilting. My legs dangled
from the air trike's backseat, smile froze
into a fixed grin after first gusts of wind.

The pilot knew every limb in the red body
of his glider. He pulled the trapeze of a control bar
(he called the "Jesus bar") to the right,
and the microlight banked to a gentle left turn.
He'd take his hands off the bar for a while,
and we would be flying straight, listening
to the rattle of our delta-wing.

Its coral, sandy, and cyan stripes suited autumnal
landscapes, challenged the greyness of coming mornings.

After we landed in high grass, the pilot and I
walked to the hangar as if we were old confidants,
even if during the flight we didn't exchange a word.
Landing, others yelled: "Initiation time!" Shots
of straight alcohol were passed across the hangar
table, and only after drinking *mit Brüderschaft,*
names of real and new pilots were announced.

The names added to the absurdity of the decrepit
post-Soviet airdrome: Oleg Vorobiev, Igor Orlov,
and Sasha Yastreb, which in English would be
a sparrow, an eagle, and a hawk.
As to my pilot whose day job in psychiatry
was revealed, he needed the wings
not less than his co-pilots, but inadvertently,
out of a habit, helped them to handle
a control bar for flying resolutions.

At least, when soon resigning from the walled factory,
I thought of the rattle of *my* delta-wing.

Photo of Elina Petrova

237

ii Light-Years of Father Kyprian

At the grotto packed with assault rifles
of *dushman* (a word in Pashto for "enemy"
and "cousin") – in the same loam coordinates
where, shortly before, his father returned
as a handful of ash in the downed Mi-8 –

an air navigator, in his first mustache,
a Russian picked cap of the mid-'80s,
steps to the quietude of a landmine field.
Kaboom! – three clinical deaths in a Kabul
hospital, dashing memories like that

of a training flight when his wing almost
shaved the Pacific to escape anti-aircraft fire.
His vision hovers along the stream of soft
light above his detached body, left below
with the remnants of his legs in a cast.

But the inexplicable calmness of that light
is so reassuring, as if it was the promise
recalled later: after he relearns to waltz
on prostheses, to jump with a parachute
back to the frontline, after he falls

in love with the bashful girl whose gaze
roaming above a party of loud pilots
stumbles onto his... She sees
that light in him even now, in their sixties,
when – in a remote Kyrgyz monastery –

he helps those, who are burned, downed
or drunk for years, to get their heads
on straight. Grey-bearded like an elder
from a Rublev icon, an air navigator –
they call him *Father Kyprian.***

Notes on Elina Petrova's poems

* - In a Russian version of Brüderschaft trinken (drinking to friendship) with arms linked at the elbows, "brothers" switch from a formal use of a capital-letter "You" with patronymic names to a simple "you" with first names.

** – Col. Valery Burkov, the last air combat officer to receive the title Hero of the Soviet Union, the highest distinction in the former U.S.S.R. He lost both legs in the war in Afghanistan, clinically died three times, survived, and returned to combat. After years of his successful governmental career, he suddenly escaped from public, and, in several years, appeared as a monk. Since 2016 he is an ordained Russian Orthodox priest, Father Kyprian.

Naba Kumar Podder
A TALE OF COLORED PENT

At the end nobody has to be detached
Nobody is only beloved as the colour
Of monochord

This tattoo time is strange too!

Is everything written in script?

Can everything rush to the utmost
Of piano---

Violin and pipe are not similar
Yet in a word they are artistic
They are fragrant Antiseptic.

Enemy doesn't test who is real
Or who is fake in the war.

What's need to react from the out?

Come to a fuss-
Pour some romance in this
Bay of Bengal.

[Translated from Bengali by Shikdar Mohammed kibriah]

Tu Niu
A FARMER'S HOMELAND

A farmer's homeland, is gathered in his palm of land
He never walks out of the crop line of sight, for his lifelong
Harvests of blossom in spring and fruit in autumn

A farmer's sweat permeates into soil, unnoticed, so –
It never stops pouring, that his piece of land
Is neither thirsty nor barren
A farmer's power is small, so –
He plows, hoes, and shoulders his rice
That his homeland is full of vigor at all times

The loud sounds of chant
Echo in the sky, so rivers and mountains
Are immersed in excitement
That they can't hold back their great joy
A farmer's intention
Never stays overnight, so he works until dawn
To uproot weeds that prevent his aspiration

A farmer's homeland is narrow, so –
He defends its territory: a village, and a few ridges
That he persists across generations, and
Keeps fostering his daughters and sons
How vast a farmer's homeland!
The Map of Rooster, hung high on the wall, daily patrolling
Records a farmer's footprints on his homeland

Britney Russell
BLACKNESS IS ROYALTY

The sun kissed my skin,
Thank God for my beautiful melanin.
Whether chestnut, almond or chocolate
Black girls are winning.

The water hugged my hair,
It appreciated the kinky flair.
My natural hair, I will perpetually wear.
It identifies who we are, whether far or near.

They planted the seed that we were always slaves.
But we were kings, queens and they were afraid:
Afraid of how powerful we were and are...
They raped Africa and left a monumental scar.

Let's take back our culture and throne!
Appreciate and love our blackness to the bone.
Rise up and discover the truth!
All along we've been lied to about our roots.

Tali Cohen Shabtai
WHO SAID CORONA?

Don't get upset because I loved
Our gone babies.
At the end of time and the universe my dream must
Be expressed

God got tired
Do you understand?

No place to travel to
As the infinity is being determined
Anew in a range of

One hundred meter
From one person to another

This outbreak is really quite sexy
Alerting, warning and killing
No better way
To laugh at the people
In such heroic way

When we celebrate our exodus
And the collapse of Pharaoh

In the spring of two thousand twenty.

Dr. Howard F. Stein
ON THIS SHORE

In Memory of Simcha Stein, 1992-1998.

We walk but for a time
On this shore.

It soothes our feet;
It swallows up
Our footprints.

It makes sand castles
Of our empires
And of our dreams.

It washes our conceits
Far out to sea.

The shore keeps us company
Until it must go on.

Sushant Thapa
BITS AND BITS

The evening has its shadow,
Its light has to be lit.
Falling of glasses and the stopping of the world
Feel the same.
Losing the mind is not same like
Losing the heart.
Heart is never insane although
It crosses the limits and beats
Across boundaries.
The doors in life can always remain open
If we know to close them.
I have lived my kind of life
My wooden bed of comfort
And my bell of joy
My stable desk of imagination
Make sure that I feel and touch
My dreams each day.
To be an answer learning to question;
The candles that wait to be worshipped
Sit and stare the retirement life of my dad.
I and my dad wish to light those candles
I can celebrate my growing older.
Much ago I began to change dreams
They do have names now.

Gita Viswanath
MY HOME

Secrets stashed away in the folds of the clothes
Like pieces of jewellery to escape a thief's eye
Vows imprinted on the walls
Alongside photo frames and stains of sweet and sour soup
Intrigues hatched behind doors
While at a game of hide and seek
Tears spurting out like water from municipal taps
When brother betrays you to mother
Laughter rising like dust and departing from the window
To the rhythms of father's stale jokes
Anger stamped hard into the floor
As the maid pounds fiery-hot red chillies
Gossip whispered in the corners of one room
only to be retched out on the floor of another
Forgiveness rolled out like a Yoga mat
To obey the slogan
Blood is thicker than water.

You are welcome to my home.
I can neither enter nor exit.

Adesokan Babatunde Waliyullah (Toonday)
FOR ALL THE 36 STATES OF POCKET VIOLENCE

In Kaduna, maybe in Benue
Bodies explode
A whole ocean of blood sluicing
down west, down east

A fume of ashes eclipses the
Raising sun, and,
To the grief of man, a blood moon

Fresh news breaks down the dead
& counts the heads of
Those whisked away like cattle

The pride stays behind, soul begging
In teary pools, degraded into
People without a government.

To the neonate, grief is a birthright
& this nation an ash tray where
Chain smokers break off the ember
Of violence

Mission Statement of New York Parrot

Our primary mission is to bridge truth and relevant information gaps between the haves and the have-nots as we liberate people from ignorance of what is happening around them and beyond borders. We culled this mission from our belief that peace, harmony and prosperous cohabitation of humans can only exist when there is fair and transparent gathering and dissemination of relevant fact-checked information for all humans regardless of their socio-economic and cultural status and orientation.

Made in the USA
Columbia, SC
05 September 2021

44937963R00137